Macondo Well
Deepwater Horizon
Blowout

LESSONS FOR IMPROVING OFFSHORE DRILLING SAFETY

Committee on the Analysis of Causes of the
Deepwater Horizon Explosion, Fire, and Oil Spill to
Identify Measures to Prevent Similar Accidents in the Future

Marine Board

Board on Environmental Studies and Toxicology

NATIONAL ACADEMY OF ENGINEERING *AND*
NATIONAL RESEARCH COUNCIL
OF THE NATIONAL ACADEMIES

THE NATIONAL ACADEMIES PRESS
Washington, D.C.
www.nap.edu

THE NATIONAL ACADEMIES PRESS   500 Fifth Street, NW   Washington, DC 20001

NOTICE: The project that is the subject of this report was approved by the Governing Board of the National Research Council, whose members are drawn from the councils of the National Academy of Sciences, the National Academy of Engineering, and the Institute of Medicine. The members of the committee responsible for the report were chosen for their special competencies and with regard for appropriate balance.

This project was supported by Contract No. N10PC18384 between the National Academy of Sciences and the U.S. Department of the Interior. Any opinions, findings, conclusions, or recommendations expressed in this publication are those of the author(s) and do not necessarily reflect the view of the organizations or agencies that provided support for this project.

International Standard Book Number-13: 978-0-309-22138-2
International Standard Book Number-10: 0-309-22138-2

Additional copies of this report are available from

The National Academies Press
500 Fifth Street, NW
Box 285
Washington, DC 20055

800-624-6242
202-334-3313 (in the Washington metropolitan area)
http://www.nap.edu

Printed in the United States of America

THE NATIONAL ACADEMIES
Advisers to the Nation on Science, Engineering, and Medicine

The **National Academy of Sciences** is a private, nonprofit, self-perpetuating society of distinguished scholars engaged in scientific and engineering research, dedicated to the furtherance of science and technology and to their use for the general welfare. Upon the authority of the charter granted to it by the Congress in 1863, the Academy has a mandate that requires it to advise the federal government on scientific and technical matters. Dr. Ralph J. Cicerone is president of the National Academy of Sciences.

The **National Academy of Engineering** was established in 1964, under the charter of the National Academy of Sciences, as a parallel organization of outstanding engineers. It is autonomous in its administration and in the selection of its members, sharing with the National Academy of Sciences the responsibility for advising the federal government. The National Academy of Engineering also sponsors engineering programs aimed at meeting national needs, encourages education and research, and recognizes the superior achievements of engineers. Dr. Charles M. Vest is president of the National Academy of Engineering.

The **Institute of Medicine** was established in 1970 by the National Academy of Sciences to secure the services of eminent members of appropriate professions in the examination of policy matters pertaining to the health of the public. The Institute acts under the responsibility given to the National Academy of Sciences by its congressional charter to be an adviser to the federal government and, upon its own initiative, to identify issues of medical care, research, and education. Dr. Harvey V. Fineberg is president of the Institute of Medicine.

The **National Research Council** was organized by the National Academy of Sciences in 1916 to associate the broad community of science and technology with the Academy's purposes of furthering knowledge and advising the federal government. Functioning in accordance with general policies determined by the Academy, the Council has become the principal operating agency of both the National Academy of Sciences and the National Academy of Engineering in providing services to the government, the public, and the scientific and engineering communities. The Council is administered jointly by both Academies and the Institute of Medicine. Dr. Ralph J. Cicerone and Dr. Charles M. Vest are chair and vice chair, respectively, of the National Research Council.

www.national-academies.org

vii

DEDICATION

We dedicate this report to the memory of the eleven people who lost their lives on board the *Deepwater Horizon* on April 20, 2010.

Jason Christopher Anderson
Aaron Dale Burkeen
Donald Neal Clark
Stephen Ray Curtis
Gordon Lewis Jones
Roy Wyatt Kemp
Karl Dale Kleppinger, Jr.
Keith Blair Manuel
Dewey Allen Revette
Shane Michael Roshto
Adam Taylor Weise

Preface

The blowout of the Macondo well on April 20, 2010, led to enormous consequences for the individuals involved in the drilling operations and for their families. Eleven workers on the *Deepwater Horizon* drilling rig lost their lives, and 16 others were seriously injured. There were also enormous consequences for the companies involved in the drilling operations, to the Gulf of Mexico environment, and to the economy of the region and beyond. The flow continued for nearly 3 months before the well could be completely killed, during which time nearly 5 million barrels of oil spilled into the gulf. The economic consequences of the event were felt almost immediately and became more widespread over time. A moratorium on drilling activities was put in place throughout the gulf, and commercial fishing was halted in much of the region. The total economic impact is in the tens of billions of dollars. The long-term ecological impact will likely take many years to measure. This was truly a "spill of national significance,"[1] and international efforts to learn from this disaster have been spurred.

Shortly after the event, the National Academy of Engineering (NAE) and the National Research Council (NRC) were asked by the Secretary of the Interior to form a committee to examine the probable causes of the *Deepwater Horizon* explosion, fire, and oil spill and to identify means for preventing similar harm in the future. The committee benefited from a focused and well-defined scope, which excluded several issues such as the extensive response and remediation efforts (see Appendix A). Nonetheless, NAE and NRC wanted to ensure that the committee had not only the requisite expertise appropriate to a deepwater drilling accident but also the breadth needed to ensure that the root causes of the incident and appropriate corrective actions could be identified. Consequently, a committee of 15 members was assembled, which provided expertise in geophysics, petroleum engineering, marine systems, accident investigations, safety systems, risk analysis, human factors, and organizational behavior (see the biographical information at the end of this document).

---

[1]Designation made by the Secretary of Homeland Security on April 29, 2010.

The committee was able to take advantage of other investigations occurring at the same time, such as the Marine Board of Investigation (MBI), convened by the U.S. Coast Guard (USCG) and the Bureau of Ocean Energy Management, Regulation, and Enforcement (BOEMRE—formerly the Minerals Management Service). Members of the committee observed the MBI hearings and reviewed documentation submitted to the board. Similarly, committee members observed hearings of the National Commission on the BP *Deepwater Horizon* Oil Spill and Offshore Drilling and the U.S. Chemical Safety Board. The committee conducted its own public meetings to hear presentations from regulators (USCG, BOEMRE, and the Republic of the Marshall Islands—the flag state), the American Petroleum Institute, the American Bureau of Shipping, and industry (see Appendix B).

The information provided to the committee by industry was constrained by the legal environment generated by the MBI, the investigation of the Department of Justice, and the prospect of multiple matters of civil litigation involving tens of billions of dollars. However, some of the companies involved in the *Deepwater Horizon* incident participated in the committee's public meetings and submitted material in writing, including several corporate investigative reports. BP, Halliburton, and Transocean provided information to the committee. Cameron, manufacturer of the *Deepwater Horizon's* blowout preventer (BOP), provided some material but declined to make a presentation on the *Deepwater Horizon* BOP.

The committee also benefited from good support by USCG, which facilitated access to recovered items from *Deepwater Horizon* (lifeboats, riser, drill pipe, and BOP). The BOP assessment was greatly aided by the forensic work performed by Det Norske Veritas (DNV) and reported by DNV (2011a, 2011b). However, the committee was unable to obtain results of Phase 2 testing of the *Deepwater Horizon* BOP led by BP. The results are maintained under protective orders by the courts supervising related litigation matters.

The committee received support from a number of industrial organizations that were not directly involved in the Macondo well–*Deepwater Horizon* incident, which improved its understanding of the various standards and practices of the industry. Of note, Shell provided access both to its Real-Time Operations Center in Houston, Texas, and to the *Deepwater Nautilus*, the sister ship to *Deepwater Horizon*. Hydril similarly provided access to its BOP design, production, and test facilities. The committee also visited Wild Well Control School in Houston to improve its understanding of the training provided to drilling personnel. In addition to the industry inputs provided through corporate channels, the committee was able to obtain inputs from industry personnel reflected in written summaries provided by the Society of Petroleum Engineers and the International Association of Drilling Contractors. The summaries were prepared with the prior understanding that none of the input would be attributed to specific individuals. To obtain a better understanding of alternative regulatory approaches, committee members visited the Petroleum Safety Authority of Norway, SINTEF (Stiftelsen for Industriell og Teknisk Forskning), the Norwegian Oil Industry Association, and the U.K. Health and Safety Executive.

The scope and depth of the information available to the committee enabled it to develop findings and informed observations concerning the probable causes (both direct and root causes) of the incident. The information also enabled the committee to develop a series of recommendations that it believes will reduce the likelihood and impact of any future well control incidents. This final report documents the major findings, observations, and recommendations developed by the committee during its study.[2] The report does not attempt to assign responsibility for the incident to specific individuals or corporations, nor does it attempt to make a systematic assessment of the extent to which the parties involved complied with applicable regulations. Such matters were deemed to be appropriately addressed by the MBI.

The committee notes that several of its recommendations reinforce steps already taken to strengthen regulatory practices in the aftermath of this incident. These are steps in the right direction, which need to be built on in a timely manner to ensure that the risks associated with this critical industry are minimized and that the public trust in both industry operations and regulatory processes is restored. Many challenges beyond those addressed in this report must be faced to revitalize the regulatory process. In particular, the administration and Congress will need to provide the funding and flexibility in hiring practices that will allow the Bureau of Safety and Environmental Enforcement (BSEE)[3] to enhance its capability and capacity.

There have been positive indications regarding industry's recognition of the need for change, as well. Notable have been the formation and funding of additional response capabilities, such as the Marine Well Containment Company. That said, the companies involved in the Macondo well–*Deepwater Horizon* incident have the added challenge of ensuring that positions taken to defend against civil liabilities and potential criminal charges do not inhibit their timely recognition of the need to change their internal processes and the manner in which the many parties to this industry (operating companies, drilling contractors, and service companies) all work together.

The need to maintain domestic sources of oil is great, but so is the need to protect the lives of those who work in this industry and to protect the Gulf of Mexico and the many other industries that depend on it. The oil and gas industry

---

[2]The committee issued an interim letter report on November 16, 2010, which presented preliminary findings and observations concerning key factors and decisions that may have contributed to the blowout of the Macondo well. The committee also provided a letter to BOEMRE on September 17, 2010, which identified potential approaches for use in conducting forensic analyses of the *Deepwater Horizon* BOP.

[3]On October 1, 2011, BOEMRE split into two entities. BSEE is currently the federal entity responsible for safety and environmental oversight of offshore oil and gas operations internal processes and the manner in which the many parties to this industry (operating companies, drilling contractors, and service companies) work together.

is robust and capable of improving offshore drilling safety; it employs many experienced personnel and utilizes many impressive technologies. Similarly, there are many dedicated and capable individuals in the various regulatory agencies responsible for overseeing the industry who can make further safety improvements. There is no reason why the diligent application of these multifold capabilities toward strengthening system safety should not significantly reduce the likelihood and consequences of any future loss of well control in the Gulf of Mexico.

Donald C. Winter, *Chair*
Committee on the Analysis of Causes of the *Deepwater Horizon* Explosion, Fire, and Oil Spill to Identify Measures to Prevent Similar Accidents in the Future

Acknowledgments

This report has been reviewed in draft form by individuals chosen for their diverse perspectives and technical expertise in accordance with procedures approved by NRC's Report Review Committee. The purpose of this independent review is to provide candid and critical comments that assist the authors and NRC in making the published report as sound as possible and to ensure that the report meets institutional standards for objectivity, evidence, and responsiveness to the study charge. The review comments and draft manuscript remain confidential to protect the integrity of the deliberative process. We thank the following individuals for their review of this report: Benton F. Baugh, Radoil Inc., Houston, Texas; Robert Bea, University of California, Berkeley (emeritus); Michael J. Burke, Tulane University, New Orleans, Louisiana; Vice Admiral James C. Card (USCG, retired), The Woodlands, Texas; Elmer Danenberger III, independent consultant, Reston, Virginia; Chan Gill, independent consultant, Avondale, Arizona; Richard Hartley, B&W Pantex, Amarillo, Texas; Trevor O. Jones, ElectroSonics Medical Inc., Cleveland, Ohio; Rear Admiral Malcolm MacKinnon III (U.S. Navy, retired), MSCL LLC, Alexandria, Virginia; Erik B. Nelson, independent consultant, Houston, Texas; Robin Pitblado, Det Norske Veritas (U.S.A.), Inc., Katy, Texas; Christopher Ranger, Ranger Consultants, Ltd., Ayrshire, Scotland; Frank J. Schuh, Drilling Technology, Inc., Plano, Texas; Richard Sears, Leading Energy Now, Houston, Texas; and A. Dan Tarlock, Chicago Kent College of Law, Chicago, Illinois.

Although the reviewers listed above provided many constructive comments and suggestions, they were not asked to endorse the committee's conclusions or recommendations, nor did they see the final draft of the report before its release. The review of this report was overseen by Robert A. Frosch, Harvard University, Cambridge, Massachusetts, and by C. Michael Walton, University of Texas, Austin. Appointed by NRC, they were responsible for making certain that an independent examination of this report was carried out in accordance with institutional procedures and that all review comments were carefully considered. Responsibility for the final content of this report rests entirely with the authoring committee and the institution.

The work of the committee was assisted by three consultants. Michael Griffes, Alexandria, Virginia, and Peter Johnson, Washington, D.C., facilitated information-gathering activities. Stephen Kemp, Marine & Process Controls LLC, Whitmore Lake, Michigan, provided analysis of the *Deepwater Horizon* control and alarm systems.

This project was overseen by the Marine Board, a component of the NRC's Transportation Research Board (TRB), with support from the Board on Environmental Studies and Toxicology of the NRC's Division on Earth and Life Studies.

Raymond Wassel managed the study under the guidance of the committee and the supervision of Stephen Godwin, Director, Studies and Special Programs, TRB. Beverly Huey and Mirsada Karalic-Loncarevic provided scientific and technical information. Norman Solomon edited the report; Jennifer Weeks prepared the prepublication manuscript, under the supervision of Javy Awan, Director of Publications, TRB. Radiah Rose assisted in preparing the prepublication manuscript and the final published version. Mark Hutchins and Orin Luke arranged meetings and provided logistical communications to the committee. In addition, Keri Schaffer helped with gathering and compiling background information.

Abbreviations

ABS	American Bureau of Shipping
ALARP	as low as reasonably practicable
AMF	automatic mode function
AoC	acknowledgment of compliance
API	American Petroleum Institute
ASRS	Aviation Safety Reporting System
BOEMRE	Bureau of Ocean Energy Management, Regulation, and Enforcement
BOP	blowout preventer
BSR	blind shear ram
BSEE	Bureau of Safety and Environmental Enforcement
CAIB	*Columbia* Accident Investigation Board
CCPS	Center for Chemical Process Safety
CDC	Centers for Disease Control and Prevention
CGD	combustible gas detector
CSB	U.S. Chemical Safety Board
CSR	casing shear ram
DHSG	*Deepwater Horizon* Study Group
DNV	Det Norske Veritas
DoD	U.S. Department of Defense
DOI	U.S. Department of the Interior
ECD	equivalent circulating density
EDS	emergency disconnect system
EIA	U.S. Energy Information Administration
EMW	equivalent mud window
EPA	U.S. Environmental Protection Agency
EPRI	Electric Power Research Institute
E&P	exploration and production
ESD	emergency shutdown
FAA	Federal Aviation Administration
FBI	Federal Bureau of Investigation
FS	flag state
GAO	U.S. General Accounting Office

HSE	Health and Safety Executive of the United Kingdom
IACS	integrated alarm and control system
IADC	International Association of Drilling Contractors
IAEA	International Atomic Energy Agency
IBOP	internal blowout preventer
LCM	lost circulation material
LMRP	lower marine riser package
MBI	Marine Board of Investigation
MGS	mud–gas separator
MMS	Minerals Management Service
MODU	mobile offshore drilling unit
MUX	multiplexer
MWCC	Marine Well Containment Company
NAE	National Academy of Engineering
NEI	Nuclear Energy Institute
NOAA	National Oceanic and Atmospheric Administration
NPC	National Petroleum Council
NRC	National Research Council
NTSB	National Transportation Safety Board
OECD	Organisation for Economic Cooperation and Development
OIM	offshore installation manager
OLF	Norwegian Oil Industry Association
ppg	pounds per gallon
Presidential Commission	National Commission on the BP *Deepwater Horizon* Oil Spill and Offshore Drilling
PSA	Petroleum Safety Authority of Norway
ROV	remotely operated vehicle
SEMS	Safety and Environmental Management Systems
SINTEF	Stiftelsen for Industriell og Teknisk Forskning
SPE	Society of Petroleum Engineers
SUBSAFE	U.S. Navy's Submarine Safety Program
TSA	Transportation Security Administration
USCG	U. S. Coast Guard
U.S. NRC	U.S. Nuclear Regulatory Commission
VBR	variable bore ram
WCID	well construction interface document

Contents

APPENDICES

BOXES, FIGURES, AND TABLES

BOX

FIGURES

TABLES

Macondo Well
Deepwater Horizon
Blowout

LESSONS FOR IMPROVING
OFFSHORE DRILLING SAFETY

Summary

This report examines the causes of the blowout of the Macondo well that occurred in the Gulf of Mexico on April 20, 2010, and provides a series of recommendations, for both the oil and gas industry and government regulators, intended to reduce the likelihood and impact of any future losses of well control during offshore drilling. The report presents the consensus view of a committee of 15 experts convened by the National Academy of Engineering (NAE), operating through the National Research Council (NRC), in response to a request from the Secretary of the U.S. Department of the Interior (DOI). The report has been subjected to a peer review in accordance with NAE–NRC procedures.

The areas of expertise of the 15 members spanned geophysics, petroleum engineering, marine systems, accident investigations, safety systems, risk analysis, human factors, and organizational behavior. This breadth of expertise enabled the committee to address both the immediate and the root causes of the various failures that led to the loss of well control and to provide a unique perspective that should complement those provided by other investigative efforts.

Offshore drilling, especially in deep water,[1] is an inherently hazardous activity. Construction of deepwater wells like Macondo is a complex process. Sophisticated equipment is used, such as the *Deepwater Horizon* drilling rig, which must operate in a highly coordinated manner in areas of uncertain geology, often under challenging environmental conditions, and subject to failures from a variety of sources including those induced by human and organizational errors. The industry has developed an impressive set of technologies to enable the construction of such wells, and it appears that viable solutions were available to address the various challenges posed by Macondo. However, the selection and application of suitable technologies will always be subject to the vagaries of the human decision-making processes, as it was in April 2010 in the Gulf of Mexico.

---

[1]For this report, the committee did not identify a specific depth to distinguish between shallow water and deep water. Although various depths have been identified by other organizations as a transition point, depths greater than 1,000 feet are often considered to define deep water.

The committee believes that material improvements to the management and safety systems used by the companies engaged in offshore oil development, along with enhancements to the regulatory regime, can and should be made, and that such efforts will materially improve all aspects of safety offshore.

THE MACONDO WELL–*DEEPWATER HORIZON* DISASTER

The Macondo well is located approximately 50 miles off the coast of Louisiana in the Mississippi Canyon region of the Gulf of Mexico. It was intended as an exploratory well, drilled to assess the presence of extractable hydrocarbons and to survey the associated reservoir structures. The well was originally planned for a total depth of 19,650 feet. A decision was made in early April 2010 to halt drilling at a total depth of 18,360 feet and prepare the well for temporary abandonment in order to utilize the well later for oil and gas production. According to BP's accident investigation report, four hydrocarbon zones had been discovered at depths ranging from 17,788 to 18,223 feet (BP 2010, 54). Furthermore, the differences between the highest reservoir pore pressure, which had to be offset by the drilling mud to prevent reservoir fluid flow, and the fracture gradients of the formation were becoming very small, leaving little margin for safe drilling. During March and April 2010, the *Deepwater Horizon* drilling team had encountered both "kicks" (hydrocarbon flows) and lost circulation events[2] (due to formation fracturing). This included a lost circulation event on April 4 at a depth of 18,260 feet (BP 2010, 17; Transocean 2011a, I, 20).

Temporary abandonment of a well intended to be used for production is a standard practice. It provides the operator time to install the substantial infrastructure needed to transport the recovered hydrocarbons to shore while releasing the expensive drilling rig for other activities. Sealing the well to ensure that no hydrocarbon flow occurs is critical to the temporary abandonment process. This is typically done through the use of cemented liners or casings, along with additional cement or mechanical plugs that provide multiple barriers to hydrocarbon flow.

The narrow margins between pore pressure and fracture gradient established a challenging environment for sealing the well. The approach chosen was to use a long-string production casing ($9\frac{7}{8} \times 7$ inches) extending from the seafloor to the bottom of the well, cemented in place with a low-density, foamed cement slurry (BP 2010, 18; Transocean 2011a, I, 27). During the cementing operation, difficulties were encountered, including those associated with converting (closing) check valves on the float collar near the bottom of the casing at 18,115 feet. Nonetheless, the drilling team determined mistakenly that the cementing operation had been completed successfully and proceeded to conduct a negative pressure test to establish the integrity of the cemented production casing. A negative pressure test, conducted by displacing some of the heavy drilling

---

[2]Lost circulation is a loss of drilling fluids into the formation.

mud with lighter seawater and checking for flow, is a standard technique for establishing the integrity of the cemented barrier. Multiple negative pressure tests were made, all of which indicated inconclusive and confusing results (BP 2010, 85; Transocean 2011a, I, 29). However, the team mistakenly determined that the negative pressure test had been conducted successfully and proceeded to abandon the well temporarily by displacing drilling mud with seawater, recovering the mud, and discharging overboard the spacer fluid that had been used in previous operations. Various anomalies were noted during this process, starting at roughly 21:00 on April 20. At approximately 21:40, mud was observed flowing onto the rig floor and well control actions were initiated, diverting flow to the mud–gas separator and activating the upper annular and upper pipe rams on the blowout preventer (BOP).

The procedures taken did not reestablish control over the well. Flammable gas alarms on the *Deepwater Horizon* sounded at approximately 21:47, followed by two explosions at approximately 21:49.

The explosions and resulting fire led to the death of 11 workers and serious injuries to 16 others. The *Deepwater Horizon* rig sank roughly 36 hours later. Nearly 5 million barrels of oil were released into the Gulf of Mexico (McNutt et al. 2011).

COMMITTEE AND ITS TASK

In response to a request from the DOI Secretary, NAE and NRC formed a committee to examine the causes of the *Deepwater Horizon*–Macondo well blowout, explosion, fire, and oil spill and to identify measures for preventing similar incidents in the future. As part of its task, the committee provided an interim letter report to the DOI Secretary on November 16, 2010. That report presented preliminary findings and observations concerning key factors and decisions that may have contributed to the blowout of the Macondo well, including engineering, testing, and maintenance procedures; operational oversight; regulatory procedures; and personnel training and certification. This final report presents the committee's overall findings with regard to the causes of the disaster and its recommended approaches for improved safety.

SUMMARY OF FINDINGS, OBSERVATIONS, AND RECOMMENDATIONS

On the basis of its assessment of the evidence collected for this final report, the committee has developed the following findings, observations, and recommendations. The sequence in which they are presented is not intended to imply a sense of priority. They are discussed in subsequent chapters of this report, along with more detailed findings, observations, and recommendations.[3]

Summary Findings

It is the committee's assessment that the following findings of facts have been established by the available evidence.

1.   The flow of hydrocarbons that led to the blowout of the Macondo well began when drilling mud was displaced by seawater during the temporary abandonment process. (Finding 2.1)[4]

2.   The decision to proceed to displacement of the drilling mud by seawater was made despite a failure to demonstrate the integrity of the cement job even after multiple negative pressure tests. This was but one of a series of questionable decisions in the days preceding the blowout that had the effect of reducing the margins of safety and that evidenced a lack of safety-driven decision making. (Finding 2.2)

3.   The reservoir formation, encompassing multiple zones of varying pore pressures and fracture gradients, posed significant challenges to isolation using casing and cement. The approach chosen for well completion failed to provide adequate margins of safety and led to multiple potential failure mechanisms. (Finding 2.3)

4.   The loss of well control was not noted until more than 50 minutes after hydrocarbon flow from the formation started, and attempts to regain control by using the BOP were unsuccessful. The blind shear ram failed to sever the drill pipe and seal the well properly, and the emergency disconnect system failed to separate the lower marine riser and the *Deepwater Horizon* from the well. (Finding 3.1)

5.   The BOP system was neither designed nor tested for the dynamic conditions that most likely existed at the time that attempts were made to recapture well control. Furthermore, the design, test, operation, and maintenance of the BOP system were not consistent with a high-reliability, fail-safe device. (Finding 3.16)

6.   Once well control was lost, the large quantities of gaseous hydrocarbons released onto the *Deepwater Horizon*, exacerbated by low wind velocity and questionable venting selection, made ignition all but inevitable. (Finding 4.1)

7.   The actions, policies, and procedures of the corporations involved did not provide an effective system safety approach commensurate with the risks of the Macondo well. The lack of a strong safety culture resulting from a defi-

---

[3]A compilation of all the report's findings, observations, and recommendations is presented in Appendix C.

[4]The first digit of a finding, observation, or recommendation refers to a chapter of this report.

cient overall systems approach to safety is evident in the multiple flawed decisions that led to the blowout. Industrial management involved with the Macondo well–*Deepwater Horizon* disaster failed to appreciate or plan for the safety challenges presented by the Macondo well. (Finding 5.1)

Summary Observations

During the course of its investigations, the committee made several observations with regard to the processes and procedures used by industry and government regulators.

1. While the geologic conditions encountered in the Macondo well posed challenges to the drilling team, alternative completion techniques and operational processes were available that could have been used to prepare the well safely for temporary abandonment. (Observation 2.1)

2. The ability of the oil and gas industry to perform and maintain an integrated assessment of the margins of safety for a complex well like Macondo is impacted by the complex structure of the offshore oil and gas industry and the divisions of technical expertise among the many contractors engaged in the drilling effort. (Observation 5.1)

3. The regulatory regime was ineffective in addressing the risks of the Macondo well. The actions of the regulators did not display an awareness of the risks or the very narrow margins of safety. (Observation 6.1)

4. The extent of training of key personnel and decision makers both in industry and in regulatory agencies has been inconsistent with the complexities and risks of deepwater drilling. (Observations 5.5 and 6.2)

5. Overall, neither the companies involved nor the regulatory community has made effective use of real-time data analysis, information on precursor incidents or near misses, or lessons learned in the Gulf of Mexico and worldwide to adjust practices and standards appropriately. (Observations 5.7 and 6.3)

6. Industry's and government's research and development efforts have been focused disproportionately on exploration, drilling, and production technologies as opposed to safety. (Observation 5.8)

Summary Recommendations

On the basis of its investigation of the Macondo well–*Deepwater Horizon* disaster and discussions with industry operating in the United States and the North Sea and with regulators from the United States, the Republic of the Marshall Islands, Australia, the United Kingdom, and Norway, the committee has developed a series of recommendations that it believes would materially improve the safety of future operations in the Gulf of Mexico.

1.   Given the critical role that margins of safety play in maintaining well control, guidelines should be established to ensure that the design approach incorporates protection against the various credible risks associated with the drilling and completion processes. (Recommendation 2.1)

2.   All primary cemented barriers to flow should be tested to verify quality, quantity, and location of cement. The integrity of primary mechanical barriers (such as the float equipment, liner tops, and wellhead seals) should be verified by using the best available test procedures. All tests should have established procedures and predefined criteria for acceptable performance and should be subject to independent, near-real-time review by a competent authority. (Recommendation 2.3)

3.   BOP systems should be redesigned to provide robust and reliable cutting, sealing, and separation capabilities for the drilling environment to which they are being applied and under all foreseeable operating conditions of the rig on which they are installed. Test and maintenance procedures should be established to ensure operability and reliability appropriate to their environment of application. Furthermore, advances in BOP technology should be evaluated from the perspective of overall system safety. Operator training for emergency BOP operation should be improved to the point that the full capabilities of a more reliable BOP can be competently and correctly employed when needed in the future. (Recommendation 3.1)

4.   Instrumentation and expert system decision aids should be used to provide timely warning of loss of well control to drillers on the rig (and ideally to onshore drilling monitors as well). If the warning is inhibited or not addressed in an appropriate time interval, autonomous operation of the blind shear rams, emergency disconnect system, general alarm, and other safety systems on the rig should occur. (Recommendations 3.5 and 4.1)

5.   Efforts to reduce the probability of future blowouts should be complemented by capabilities of mitigating the consequences of a loss of well control. Industry should ensure timely access to demonstrated well-capping and containment capabilities. (Recommendation 5.6)

6.   The United States should fully implement a hybrid regulatory system that incorporates a limited number of prescriptive elements into a proactive, goal-oriented risk management system for health, safety, and the environment. (Recommendation 6.1)

7.   The Bureau of Safety and Environmental Enforcement (BSEE) of the U.S. Department of the Interior and other regulators should identify and enforce safety-critical points during well construction and abandonment that warrant explicit regulatory review and approval before operations can proceed. (Recommendation 6.6)

8.   A single U.S. government agency should be designated with responsibility for ensuring an integrated approach for system safety for all offshore drilling activities. (Recommendation 6.15)

9.   Operating companies should have ultimate responsibility and accountability for well integrity, because only they are in a position to have visibil-

ity into all its aspects. Operating companies should be held responsible and accountable for well design, well construction, and the suitability of the rig and associated safety equipment. Notwithstanding the above, the drilling contractor should be held responsible and accountable for the operation and safety of the offshore equipment. (Recommendations 5.1 and 6.20)

10. Industry should greatly expand R&D efforts focused on improving the overall safety of offshore drilling in the areas of design, testing, modeling, risk assessment, safety culture, and systems integration. Such efforts should encompass well design, drilling and marine equipment, human factors, and management systems. These endeavors should be conducted to benefit the efforts of industry and government to instill a culture of safety. (Recommendation 5.2)

11. Industry, BSEE, and other regulators should undertake efforts to expand significantly the formal education and training of personnel engaged in offshore drilling to support proper implementation of system safety. (Recommendations 5.3 and 6.23)

12. Industry, BSEE, and other regulators should improve corporate and industrywide systems for reporting safety-related incidents. Reporting should be facilitated by enabling anonymous or "safety privileged" inputs. Corporations should investigate all such reports and disseminate their lessons-learned findings in a timely manner to all their operating and decision-making personnel and to the industry as a whole. A comprehensive lessons-learned repository should be maintained for industrywide use. This information can be used for training in accident prevention and continually improving standards. (Recommendations 5.4 and 6.14)

13. Industry, BSEE, and other regulators should foster an effective safety culture through consistent training, adherence to principles of human factors, system safety, and continued measurement through leading indicators. (Recommendations 5.5 and 6.25)

On the basis of the available evidence, the committee has identified the principal causes of the incident, as summarized above and described in the report in greater detail. Certain factors, such as the complete hydrocarbon flow path, may never be definitively identified, since the requisite forensic evidence lies more than 2 miles beneath the seabed. Similarly, many questions concerning the *Deepwater Horizon* rig will remain unanswerable so long as it lies on the bottom of the Gulf of Mexico, with its equipment unavailable for inspection and data recorders unreadable. Furthermore, the loss of several of the workers involved in the pivotal decisions on the *Deepwater Horizon* limits inquiry into the causes and rationale involved in those decisions. Even so, the committee believes that it was able to identify and assess the principal direct and root causes of the incident and develop a series of recommendations that would provide suitable and cost-effective corrective actions, materially reducing the likelihood of a similar event in the future.

1

Introduction

The offshore drilling industry has made tremendous technological strides since a freestanding structure for drilling was built in 1937 in the Gulf of Mexico in 14 feet of water, more than a mile offshore.[1] Ten years later, the first productive well located out of sight of land was drilled from a fixed platform located 10.5 miles off the Louisiana coast. During the 1950s, drilling rigs with mobile platforms, "jacked up" out of the water by supporting legs resting on the seafloor, were able to drill into water depths exceeding 100 feet. By 1957, 23 drilling units were operating in the gulf.

Mobile offshore drilling units (MODUs) allowed for drilling while floating in place without the use of supporting legs. The first drillship was introduced in the 1950s; the first semisubmersible rig was introduced in the early 1960s. Semisubmersible rigs on location are designed to have a larger proportion of their mass and structure below the water surface for greater stability against wind and waves.

Use of MODUs in deeper water required operations that were more complex than those practiced on fixed platform rigs. For example, longer and heavier riser systems were needed for the transfer of fluids between the rig and the seafloor. Also, the operation and maintenance of the blowout preventer (BOP) system[2] on the seafloor became more difficult under the harsh conditions directly at the seafloor.[3]

Continued advances in geologic exploration techniques, well designs, and recording of key geologic information enabled drilling operations to expand into

---

[1]This overview of the technological advances in offshore drilling is based on information provided in the final report of the Presidential Commission (2011) and the references cited therein. See Chief Counsel (2011) for background information and illustrations on offshore drilling operations.

[2]Among other functions, the BOP system is used to confine hydrocarbon fluids that unexpectedly enter into the borehole from the geologic formation during drilling operations (see Chapter 3).

[3]Jackup rigs typically use surface BOP systems. However, floating rigs have used surface BOP systems only sparingly.

deeper water. For example, in the 1960s digital sound recording and processing greatly enhanced the quality and interpretability of seismic data. In the 1970s advances were made in digital, three-dimensional seismic imaging, and in the 1980s use of computer workstations enabled faster processing of the data generated in geologic surveys. Those and other technological advances dramatically enhanced industry's accuracy in locating productive wells. Improved accuracy was a critical factor, given the multimillion dollar cost of drilling an individual well in deep water. Between 1985 and 1997, the success rate of offshore exploratory wells for the major companies in the United States increased from 36 to 51 percent (EIA 2008).

New generations of rigs were developed that enabled drilling at water depths of 5,000 to 10,000 feet, and from 20,000 to 30,000 feet of subseafloor depth. Advanced drilling techniques allowed the direction of an individual well to be changed from vertical to horizontal for greater adaptability to geologic conditions. Techniques were also developed to obtain information (such as position, temperature, pressure, and porosity data) from within the borehole while the well was being drilled.

By 1990, most of the oil and gas from the Gulf of Mexico came from wells drilled through an average production-weighted depth of about 250 feet of water. By 1998, the average production-weighted depth of water was greater than 1,000 feet. At that point, deepwater production (at about 700,000 barrels of oil and 2 billion cubic feet of gas per day) surpassed that from shallow water for the first time.

Global deepwater production capacity increased by more than threefold from 2000 to 2009 (from 1.5 million barrels per day in water depths over 2,000 feet to more than 5 million barrels per day). In 2008, total oil and gas discovered in deep water globally exceeded the volume found onshore and in shallow water combined.

CHALLENGES IN DESIGNING AND
CONSTRUCTING OFFSHORE WELLS

Geologic structures beneath the deep water[4] of the Gulf of Mexico provide a harsh and unpredictable environment of high-temperature and high-pressure hydrocarbon reservoirs that typically contain significant amounts of dissolved natural gas. These factors require additional precautions in the design and construction of wells.

The formation fracture pressure (the pressure at which a hydraulic fracture forms at the wellbore and propagates out into the formation) usually increases

---

[4]For this report, the committee did not identify a specific depth to distinguish between shallow water and deep water. Although various depths have been identified by other organizations as a transition point, depths greater than 1,000 feet are often considered to define deep water.

with depth, as does the pore pressure (the pressure exerted by the saline water or hydrocarbons in the pore space of rock).[5] Rig personnel use dense fluids during drilling (i.e., drilling mud) and different types of barriers inside the well after drilling to control subsurface pressure and prevent unintended hydrocarbon flow from geologic formations into the wellbore.

As the well is being drilled, drilling mud is pumped into the drill pipe connected to a drill bit. Mud flows out of nozzles in the bit and then circulates back to the rig through the space between the drill pipe and the sides of the well (the annular space), carrying away cutting debris and cooling and lubricating the bit and wellbore. In addition, drilling mud is used to control pressures inside the wellbore.

The pore fluids are contained in the reservoir rock by using the weight of a column of drilling mud to create hydrostatic pressure at the reservoir that is higher than the pore pressure. The crew monitors and adjusts the mud weight to keep the pressure exerted by the mud inside the wellbore between the pore pressure and the fracture pressure. Should the mud weight be lower than the pore pressure, an undesired flow of reservoir fluids will enter the wellbore (an event known as a kick). If a kick occurs, a blowout could result if proper well control procedures are not followed.

As the well is drilled deeper, an increase in the mud weight may be necessary to prevent kicks. However, the mud weight must not be so high that the hydrostatic pressure in the wellbore exceeds the fracturing pressure of the exposed rock at any point in the wellbore. If a fracture occurs, drilling mud will flow out of the well into the geologic formation so that mud returns are lost instead of circulating back to the surface. Should lost circulation occur, drilling cannot be continued until the mud losses are stopped. Severe lost circulation can cause the pressure in the well to become too low to prevent reservoir fluids from entering the wellbore. The well may also become unstable and collapse.

The fracture pressure and pore pressure can be difficult to predict in advance of drilling the well, and some formations in the Gulf of Mexico have pore pressures and fracture gradients that can be either higher or lower than anticipated. The pore pressure can be close to the fracture pressure, as was seen in drilling the Macondo well, presenting a substantial challenge to the overall safety of the drilling operation (see Chapter 2).

For cases where the pore pressure is close to the fracture pressure, which is common in the deep water of the Gulf of Mexico, attention is paid to any increases in well pressure that might be caused by drill pipe movement or pumping fluids. Each of these factors can cause the pressure in the wellbore to exceed the fracture pressure, creating well control problems such as lost circulation and possibly a kick.

---

[5]Additional information about designing and constructing offshore wells is given by sources such as Maclachlan (2007), Bommer (2008), and Zoback (2010).

Shallower formations left exposed in the wellbore may not be capable of withstanding the growing pressure caused by increased mud weight and could hydraulically fracture. When drilling mud can no longer be relied on for primary well control, the crew stops drilling and installs steel casing into the wellbore to protect the shallower, weaker formations. A casing string is composed of sections of steel pipe that are screwed together. The bottom portion of the casing string is sealed by pumping a cement slurry down the casing and out into the annulus. When the cement sets, the weaker formations above the end of the casing are isolated from the higher pressures that will be encountered as the well is drilled deeper. Cement also serves to support and anchor the casing to the formation. The intent is to prevent fluids from flowing up the annular space outside the casing.

Casing is also used to isolate the final section of a well once it has been finished. This stabilizes the last open section of the well and allows for the later production of fluids from selected reservoirs. The cement forms a plug in the very bottom of the casing that would otherwise remain open. This final string of casing can extend back to the surface of the well (in this case the wellhead that was installed at the ocean floor) or can be suspended or hung from the end of the previously run casing string.

The rig crew uses additional barriers inside the well to augment the primary barrier system. For example, check valves (a float collar or a float shoe, or both) are installed at the bottom of the casing string. They are intended to prevent flow back into the casing while the cement is setting or in case the cement seal fails. Also, the top of the casing is sealed inside the wellhead or the hanger so that fluids cannot escape past the top of the casing should the cement seal fail in the annulus. Finally, some form of well control cap is placed on top of the wellhead to prevent or control flow out of the casing. During drilling and casing installation, a BOP system is used. In an emergency situation, the BOP system can be activated to seal an open well, close the annular portion of the well around the drill pipe or casing, or cut through the drill pipe with steel shearing blades and then seal the well. A typical BOP system also has more routine functions such as enabling certain pressure tests to assess well integrity and injecting and removing fluid from the well through its "choke" and "kill" lines, which are high-pressure lines running between the BOP and the rig.

After the well is completed, the BOP is replaced by a production control assembly (often called the "Christmas tree" or "tree"). These systems are designed to provide redundant control of the well and prevent unwanted flows from the reservoirs. The integrity of the barriers can be evaluated by pressure tests and by taking measurements with various instruments (logging). If there is a delay between finishing drilling operations and commencing completion operations, the well is temporarily abandoned by setting mechanical or cement plugs inside the casing.

SEVERAL PAST ACCIDENTS CAUSED BY BLOWOUTS

The Macondo well–*Deepwater Horizon* incident on April 20, 2010, was not the first major blowout associated with offshore drilling (Presidential Commission Staff 2011). Past incidents involving blowouts include the following:

- On January 28, 1969, a blowout occurred at a well located in the Santa Barbara Channel and lasted 11 days. The ultimate release of oil amounted to between 80,000 and 100,000 barrels (Kallman and Wheeler 1984). A failure to keep the hydrostatic pressure in the well greater than the pore pressure resulted in the flow of hydrocarbons into the well. Attempts to control the well led to blowouts in the immediate surrounding area through several breaches in the geologic formation that extended up through the mud line (County of Santa Barbara 2005).

- On June 3, 1979, the Ixtoc I well blowout in Mexico's Bay of Campeche took 9 months to cap and released an estimated 3.5 million barrels of oil. The formation at the bottom of the well was fractured, causing the loss of mud. Hydrostatic pressure for control of the well was lost after the drill string was pulled out of the borehole. The BOP failed to secure the well because the thick, large-diameter drill collars were inside the BOP stack and prevented the shear rams from cutting the pipe and the pipe rams from closing around the large-diameter pipe.

- On August 21, 2009, a blowout occurred at the Montara Wellhead Platform located off the northwest Australian coast in the Timor Sea. The cement in the well and the float equipment failed to prevent flow from the reservoir into the casing. When the temporary well cap was removed to begin completion operations, the BOP was not installed. This left the well open and flow began from the reservoir, eventually reaching the surface where it could not be controlled. The operator estimated that 400 barrels of crude oil were lost per day. The uncontrolled release continued until November 3, 2009, and response operations continued until December 3, 2009. An investigation found that the operating company "did not observe sensible oilfield practices at the Montara Oilfield. Major shortcomings in the operating company's procedures were widespread and systemic, directly leading to the blowout" (Borthwick 2010).

Several other major accidents associated with offshore drilling and production that stemmed from causes other than a well blowout are discussed in Chapters 5 and 6.

HISTORY OF MACONDO WELL BEFORE THE BLOWOUT[6]

On March 19, 2008, BP obtained a 10-year lease to Mississippi Canyon

---

[6]Details are based on information presented by BP (2010), DHSG (2011), Presidential Commission (2011), and others (see Box 1-1).

Block 252 in Central Gulf of Mexico Lease Sale 206, which was conducted by the Minerals Management Service (MMS). Ownership of the lease was shared among BP (65 percent), Anadarko Petroleum (25 percent) and MOEX Offshore (10 percent). As the lease operator, BP was the company responsible for carrying out the operations.

On April 6, 2008, MMS approved the exploration plan for the lease, a revised exploration plan on April 16, and an Application for Permit to Drill the Macondo Well on May 22. In addition, because of the well conditions, BP submitted Applications for Permit to Modify that were approved by MMS at various points during the drilling program.

Initial drilling of the Macondo well began on October 6, 2009, with Transocean's semisubmersible MODU *Marianas* in a water depth of greater than 5,000 feet. Drilling was halted about a month later on November 8 as the *Marianas* was secured and evacuated for Hurricane Ida. The *Marianas* was subsequently removed after sustaining hurricane damage that required dock repairs. After the repairs, the rig was not returned to drill the Macondo well.

The *Deepwater Horizon* was selected in January 2010 to finish drilling the Macondo well. The rig was owned and operated by Transocean and had been under contract to BP in the Gulf of Mexico for approximately 9 years. MMS approved an Application for a Revised New Well on January 14, the Macondo plan was updated, and drilling activities began on February 6.

Subsequent activities leading up to the blowout, explosions, and fire are discussed in the following chapters of this report.

COMMITTEE'S APPROACH TO ITS TASK

The two main components of the committee's task were to examine the causes of the Macondo well–*Deepwater Horizon* incident and to identify measures for preventing similar incidents in the future. Offshore drilling is a safety-critical process that warrants a safety system commensurate with the overall risk presented. In that light, the committee considered key factors and decisions that may have contributed to the blowout of the Macondo well, including engineering, testing, and maintenance procedures; operational oversight; regulatory procedures; and personnel training and certification. The committee examined the extent to which there were margins of safety to allow for uncertainties in the interactions of equipment, humans, procedures, and the environment under normal and adverse conditions. The committee developed overall findings of fact related to the incident, observations concerning contributing factors, and recommendations intended to reduce the likelihood and impact of any future well control incidents.[7] They are presented in the aggregate in the report summary. The committee also presented more detailed findings, observations, and recom-

---

[7]The findings and observations provide context for the recommendations, but there is not a one-to-one correspondence.

mendations on well design and construction, the BOP system, MODUs, industry management of offshore drilling, and regulatory oversight in Chapters 2 through 6, respectively.[8]

Well Design and Construction

To identify causative factors for the blowout, the committee examined the design of the Macondo well, the processes for developing the well design and for making subsequent changes, and the construction of the well. Particular attention was given to the reported narrow range between pore pressure and fracture gradient (BP 2010) because of the challenges this presents. Attention was also given to the approach selected to temporarily abandon the well given these conditions. A number of key decisions related to the design, construction, and testing of the barriers critical to the temporary abandonment process were examined and found to be flawed. Recommendations for achieving a more robust approach to implementing and verifying the needed barriers are provided (see Chapter 2).

BOP System

Once the rig crew realized that hydrocarbons were flowing into the well, the BOP system did not recapture well control. The committee tracked the forensic analysis of the BOP arranged by the Marine Board of Investigation[9] and considered key factors that affected the performance of the BOP system during the blowout. The committee also considered the findings of past evaluations of the reliability of BOP systems under real-world conditions. Chapter 3 reports on the extent to which the design, testing, and maintenance of the *Deepwater Horizon* BOP system were commensurate with a high-reliability fail-safe mechanism within an overall safety system. The chapter also provides the committee's recommendations for improving the reliability of BOP systems.

Mobile Offshore Drilling Unit

Except for the BOP system, there was no evidence implicating the *Deepwater Horizon* MODU as a causative factor in the blowout. However, there were concerns that aspects of the rig design and operation may have contributed to the

---

[8]A compilation of all the report's findings, observations, and recommendations is presented in Appendix C.

[9]The Marine Board of Investigation (sometimes referred to as the Joint Investigation Team) was conducted by the U.S. Department of the Interior's Bureau of Ocean Energy Management, Regulation, and Enforcement and the U.S. Coast Guard to develop conclusions and recommendations as they relate to the *Deepwater Horizon* MODU explosion and loss of life.

casualties of the workers. Furthermore, the loss of the rig may have limited options for recapturing control of the well. These concerns led to the assessments and recommendations reported in Chapter 4.

Industry Management of Offshore Drilling

The multiple companies involved in drilling the Macondo well reflect the complex structure of the offshore oil and gas industry and the division of technical expertise among the many contractors engaged in the drilling effort. Chapter 5 reports on the committee's assessment of the extent to which the actions, policies, and procedures of corporations involved failed to provide an effective systems-safety approach commensurate with risks of the Macondo well. The committee noted that the safe drilling of deepwater wells is inherently dependent on human decision making. Therefore, there is a critical need for adequately trained personnel. The committee assessed the education, training, and certification of key personnel and the extent of industrywide learning from past events that have led to—or avoided—well control incidents. The chapter also provides recommendations for improving various aspects of industry management.

Regulatory Reform

In 2010, the regulatory approach used by MMS was based primarily on prescriptive regulations concerning well design, drilling equipment, well construction, and testing. This approach proved to be inadequate, as evidenced by the Macondo well blowout and the actions that led to the loss of well control. The committee noted the inherent limitations of prescriptive approaches and the progress on goal-oriented regulatory processes being implemented for drilling in the North Sea, Australia, and elsewhere. The approach in the United States is now shifting to be more goal-oriented and less prescriptive. Also, a process of administrative restructuring of MMS began in May 2010. The Bureau of Safety and Environmental Enforcement is currently the federal entity responsible for safety and environmental oversight of offshore oil and gas operations. In Chapter 6, the committee identifies key enhancements needed as regulatory reform proceeds.

OTHER INVESTIGATIONS

Additional background discussions of topics related to the Macondo well–*Deepwater Horizon* incident are provided in other recent reports (see Box 1-1). The results of these investigations were helpful in informing the committee's deliberations. Presentations made to the committee are listed in Appendix B.

BOX 1-1 Reports of Other Macondo Well–*Deepwater Horizon*
Investigations (*Listed in Chronological Order*)

May 2010. DOI. *Increased Safety Measures for Energy Development on the Outer Continental Shelf for 30 CFR Part 250* ("30-day report"). http://www.boemr e.gov/eppd/PDF/EAInterimSafetyRule.pdf.

September 2010. BP. *Deepwater Horizon Accident Investigation Report.* http://www. bp.com/liveassets/bp_internet/globalbp/globalbp_uk_english/gom_response/ST AGING/local_assets/downloads_pdfs/Deepwater_Horizon_Accident_Investigati on_Report.pdf.

January 2011. National Commission on the BP Deepwater Horizon Oil Spill and Offshore Drilling. *Deep Water: The Gulf Oil Disaster and the Future of Offshore Drilling.* http://www.oilspillcommission.gov/sites/default/files/documents/ DEEPWATER_ReporttothePresident_FINAL.pdf.

February 2011. Chief Counsel. *Macondo: The Gulf Oil Disaster.* Chief Counsel's Report, National Commission on the BP Deepwater Horizon Oil Spill and Offshore Drilling. http://www.oilspillcommission.gov/sites/default/files/documents/ C21462-408_CCR_for_web_0.pdf.

March 2011. DHSG. *Final Report on the Investigation of the Macondo Well Blowout.* http://ccrm.berkeley.edu/pdfs_papers/bea_pdfs/DHSGFinalReport-March2011- tag.pdf.

March 2011. DNV. *Forensic Examination of Deepwater Horizon Blowout Preventer, Vol. I and II (Appendices).* Final Report for U.S. Department of the Interior, Bureau of Ocean Energy Management, Regulation, and Enforcement, Washington, D.C. Report No. EP030842. http://www.boemre.gov/pdfs/maps/DNVReportVol I.pdf, http://www.uscg.mil/hq/cg5/cg545/dw/exhib/DNV%20BOP%20report% 20-%20Vol%202%20%282%29.pdf.

April 2011. USCG. *Report of Investigation into the Circumstances Surrounding the Explosion, Fire, Sinking and Loss of Eleven Crew Members Aboard the Mobile Offshore Drilling Unit Deepwater Horizon in the Gulf of Mexico April 20-22, 2010, Vol. I.* https://www.hsdl.org/?view&did=6700.

April 2011. DNV. *Addendum to Final Report: Forensic Examination of Deepwater Horizon Blowout Preventer.* Report No. EP030842. http://www.boemre.gov/pd fs/maps/AddendumFinal.pdf.

June 2011. Transocean. *Macondo Well Incident. Transocean Investigation Report Vol. I and II* (Appendices). http://www.deepwater.com/fw/main/Public-Report- 1076.html.

August 2011. Republic of the Marshall Islands Office of the Maritime Administrator. *Deepwater Horizon Marine Casualty Investigation Report.* Office of the Maritime Administrator. http://www.register-iri.com/forms/upload/Republic_of_the_ Marshall_Islands_DEEPWATER_HORIZON_Marine_Casualty_Investigation_ Report-Low_Resolution.pdf.

September 2011. BOEMRE. *Report Regarding the Causes of the April 20, 2010 Macondo Well Blowout.* http://www.boemre.gov/pdfs/maps/dwhfinal.pdf.

2

Well Design and Construction

The design and construction of a well are crucial to the safe exploration for and extraction of oil and gas resources. The process becomes more complex as the operating environment becomes harsher, as in deep, high-pressure, high-temperature wells drilled into the seabed beneath deep water. Macondo was such a well, with a total depth of more than 18,300 feet below sea level in slightly more than 5,000 feet of seawater. This chapter discusses changes that were made to the original Macondo well plan in response to geologic conditions encountered while drilling progressed. It then focuses attention on the approaches selected for temporary abandonment[1] of the well given these conditions. The chapter provides findings and observations concerning a number of key decisions related to the design, construction, and testing of the barriers critical to the temporary abandonment process.[2] At the end of the chapter, recommendations for achieving a more robust approach for implementing and verifying needed barriers are provided.

OVERVIEW OF THE MACONDO WELL PLAN

Macondo was an exploration well designed so that it could later be completed for production if sufficient hydrocarbons were found. The initial objective was to evaluate Miocene age formations expected to be found between 18,000 and 19,000 feet below sea level in about 5,000 feet of water. The original well plan was to drill to a total depth of 19,650 feet, but this was modified during drilling and the actual total depth was 18,360 feet, as discussed below. Before the well was drilled, design teams estimated pore pressures and strengths of geo-

---

[1]Temporary abandonment refers to a set of normal procedures used by rig personnel to secure a well after drilling has been completed, so that the rig, along with its blowout preventer and marine riser, can be moved from the well site. The *Deepwater Horizon* was to leave the Macondo well and another rig was to be used to prepare the well for production at some later time.

[2]Detailed descriptions of the overall sequence involved in constructing and testing the integrity of Macondo well barriers are provided in various reports listed in Box 1-1 of Chapter 1.

logic formations to create a design that included elements such as drilling procedures, drilling mud, drill bits, casing design, cement, and testing.

The original plan, shown in Figure 2-1, called for eight casing strings and
liners (each consisting of steel casing segments that were screwed together), but
the plan was modified to react to conditions that were encountered during drilling. Drilling ceased at 18,360 feet (a shallower depth than planned) and involved
the use of a total of nine casing strings and liners, rather than the planned eight,
including the final $9\,\frac{7}{8}$- × 7-inch tapered production casing (sometimes referred
to as a "long string") as shown in Figure 2-2. The well was to be temporarily
plugged and abandoned after the production casing was set and then completed
for production at a later date.

The Macondo well presented a number of technical challenges to the drilling and completion teams, including the deep water, high formation pressures,
and the need to drill through multiple geologic zones of varying pore and fracture pressures. In general, many of these problems can be anticipated, but some,
such as pore and fracture pressure, are difficult to estimate in advance of drilling
the well. This is especially true for the first well drilled in a new area, as was the
case for Macondo. Thus, adaptation of the original well plan to the changing
conditions encountered with depth when the well is drilled is not unusual. It is
critical that the design be adapted to changing conditions with sufficient margins
of safety to allow for further uncertainties that may be encountered during the
operation.

Wellbore events that necessitated changes to the Macondo well plan included the following (BP 2010, 17-22):

1.   Measurements showed that pore pressures were increasing at a faster
rate than anticipated, combined with a period of lost circulation of drilling mud
at 12,350 feet, indicating that the well could not be continued without setting
protective casing. The 16-inch liner was set at 11,585 feet to seal off this section
of the well. The setting depth of this liner was 915 feet shallower than planned.

2.   In the course of drilling at 13,250 feet, a kick occurred, and the lower
annular blowout preventer (BOP) was closed in response. During well control
operations, the drill string became stuck and was severed at 12,147 feet. The
drill string and hole below 12,147 feet were abandoned, and subsequent well
drilling deviated slightly to go around the abandoned materials left in the original hole. The $13\,\frac{5}{8}$-inch liner was run at 13,145 feet, which was shallower than
planned, to allow the well to be drilled safely past the higher-pressure reservoir
that had been encountered. The $11\,\frac{7}{8}$-inch liner was used at 15,103 feet to seal
the reservoir and allow for the use of higher mud weights than had been anticipated. Mud weight was to be kept between the curves for pore pressure and fracture pressure, as shown in Figure 2-3.

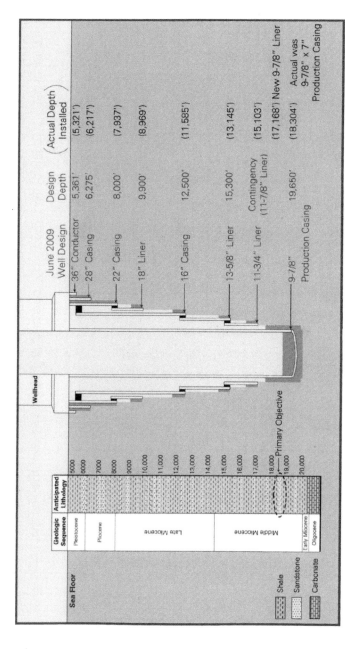

FIGURE 2-1 Original wellbore architecture planned for Macondo well. Source: BP 2010, p. 16. Reprinted with permission; copyright 2010, BP.

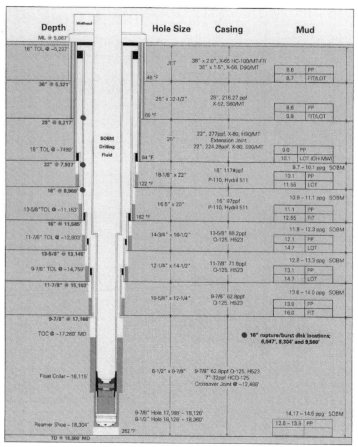

FIGURE 2-2 Final wellbore architecture for Macondo well. Source: BP 2010, p. 19. Reprinted with permission; copyright 2010, BP.

    3.   The 9 $\frac{7}{8}$-inch casing (originally planned as the production casing) was used as a liner at 17,168 feet to drill the final section of the well safely, where the use of higher mud weights was expected in continuing the well to the planned depth of 19,650 feet.

    4.   During drilling at 18,250 feet, severe lost circulation of drilling mud occurred. This problem was solved by the use of mud containing material designed to stop lost circulation and by a reduction of mud weight from 14.3 to 14.1 pounds per gallon (ppg). The lower mud weight should not have been needed at this depth on the basis of the original plan and was an indication that pore pressure and fracture pressure in part of this interval were considerably less than had been anticipated.

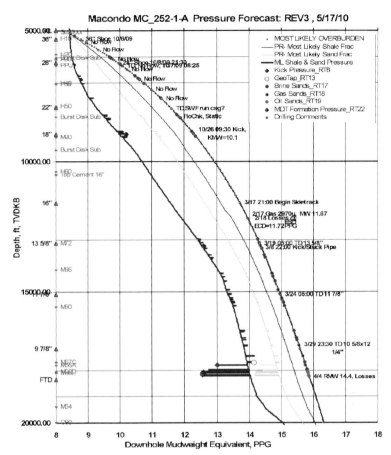

FIGURE 2-3 The four curves (moving from right to left) represent overburden stress, fracture gradients in the shale and sands, and pore pressure in the Macondo well. Depth and diameter values on the y-axis correspond to the final well bore architecture shown in Figure 2-2. The equivalent mud weight (EMW), expressed in pounds per gallon (ppg), must be higher than the pore pressure to avoid flow from the well and lower than the fracture gradient to prevent accidental hydraulic fracturing. Note the small separation between the values at depths below 18,000 feet. Source: BP unpublished report, July 26, 2010.[3] Reprinted with permission, BP.

5.   The well was drilled to 18,360 feet, and after 5 days of logging to make a detailed record of the geologic formations, it was determined that hydrocarbon-bearing reservoirs of sufficient quality existed to warrant completion of the well for production at a later time. According to the BP accident investiga-

---

[3]BP Post-Well Subsurface Description of Macondo well (MC0252_1BP1) v3. July 26, 2010.

tion report, the well analysis indicated that there were in fact several reservoirs open in the wellbore with decreasing pore pressure with depth, as shown in Figure 2-4. The hydrocarbon reservoirs had pore pressures equivalent to a range of 12.6 to 13.1 ppg. A reservoir containing salt water that had a pore pressure equivalent to 14.1 ppg was also exposed in the wellbore. As discussed below, the difference between the mud weight needed to prevent flow of salt water and the mud weight above which reservoir fracture could occur was only 0.2 ppg. Recent reports in the press have indicated that a thin gas sand was present above the salt water bearing zone shown in Figure 2-4 and have questioned the possible contribution of this sand to the blowout. The committee has seen no evidence indicating that flow occurred upwards in the annulus between the production casing and the reservoirs (see discussion below). Also, the presence of the high-pressure salt water sand created the same completion problem referenced above as would have been created by the presence of a high-pressure gas sand. Therefore, the presence or absence of the gas sand is expected to have had no material effect on the cause of the blowout.

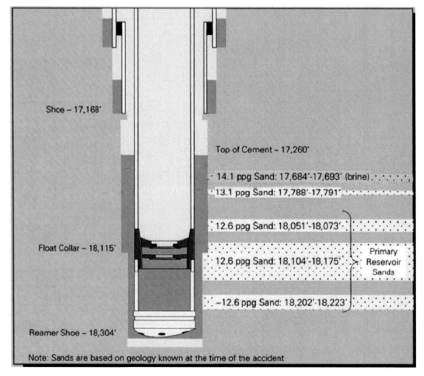

FIGURE 2-4 Variation of pore pressure in the open hole section of the Macondo well expressed in pounds per gallon. Source: BP 2010, p. 54. Reprinted with permission; copyright 2010, BP.

To continue drilling to the planned final depth of 19,650 feet, the reservoirs that had been discovered with decreasing pore and fracture pressures with depth (Figure 2-4) were to be sealed with the 9 $\frac{7}{8}$- × 7-inch combination casing string and cement. However, because the hole diameter that could be drilled below the 7-inch casing was considered too small to be practical, the well was terminated at 18,360 feet.

The challenge then was to install the production casing and pump the cement into the well without causing additional lost circulation. This was achieved on the basis of reports from the rig that no lost circulation occurred during casing and cementing operations (BP 2010, 23).

Once the casing and cementing operations were concluded, the focus moved to the installation and testing of the integrity of the wellhead seals and testing of the integrity of the cement, and then to completion of the temporary abandonment process.

FINDINGS

Beginning of Hydrocarbon Flow That Led to the Blowout

As part of the temporary abandonment process, a negative pressure test was used to indicate whether a cement barrier and other flow barriers had isolated formation fluids from the wellbore. To conduct the test, rig personnel purposely reduced the hydrostatic pressure inside the well. If the barriers were effective, there should be no flow into the well (or pressure buildup) from the formation during the test. After deciding (incorrectly) that the negative pressure test indicated that the barriers were effective, rig personnel continued with the temporary abandonment process. The annular BOP was opened, and seawater was circulated down the drill pipe and up the casing and marine riser to the surface. Seawater displaced the mud from the marine riser and from the well to a depth of 8,367 feet (measured from the rig). This had the effect of reducing the hydrostatic pressure in the well below the reservoir pressure. Because the cement and mechanical barriers did not have sufficient integrity (as discussed below), hydrocarbons began to flow from the formation into the well.

Summary Finding 2.1: **The flow of hydrocarbons that led to the blowout of the Macondo well began when drilling mud was displaced by seawater during the temporary abandonment process.**

Misinterpretation of Cement Integrity Test Results

The negative pressure test was attempted three times, as described in the BP accident investigation report (BP 2010). The initial test was flawed because the annular BOP did not seal and allowed 50 barrels (bbl) of heavy 16-ppg spacer fluid—made up of lost circulation material (LCM)—to flow back into the well below the BOP. This was recognized by rig personnel, and the closing pressure on the annular BOP was increased to make a seal. At the end of this first test, the drill pipe pressure was 273 pounds per square inch (psi) and the kill line pressure was zero with both lines shut in.

In the second test after increasing the closing pressure on the BOP, the drill pipe pressure increased to 1,250 psi. The drill pipe was opened and the pressure decreased to zero after flowing out more water than was necessary to account for mud compressibility. The drill pipe pressure should not have built up between tests, but this could have been attributed to the heavy mud leaking past the annular BOP. The mud volume that flowed out beyond what was necessary to account for mud compressibility should have made this test a failure, despite the drill pipe pressure having bled to zero.

With the drill pipe shut in, the kill line was chosen for the third test. It was opened, and it flowed out between 3 and 15 bbl of water and was shut in. During this time the drill pipe pressure slowly built up to 1,400 psi and stabilized.

The kill line was confirmed to be full of water and then reopened. It flowed out a small volume, and then flow out of the kill line ceased. The open kill line was monitored for 30 minutes with no pressure and no flow. Possible reasons for this are the following: the kill line may have been plugged by the LCM spacer, the pressure might have been equalized by the flow of the dense spacer into the kill line, or the correct valves for the kill line may not have been opened during this final test. The drill pipe maintained 1,400 psi.

Rig personnel focused on the fact that no flow was coming out of the kill line instead of addressing the implications of the shut in pressure having built up on the drill pipe. After some discussion on the rig, the negative test was deemed a success. However, the pressure buildup actually meant that the test had failed. The explanation used on the rig was an erroneous theory referred to as the "bladder effect" (see BOEMRE 2011, 95). The term, as used in the industry, is unrelated to the situation faced during the negative pressure test.

At this point the annular preventer was opened. When this was done, the marine riser was still full of 14-ppg mud and 16-ppg LCM spacer, which was sufficient to offset the reservoir pressure. Circulation of seawater was continued, displacing the mud from the riser and steadily decreasing the hydrostatic pressure inside the well. As mentioned above, when the hydrostatic pressure from the seawater and mud became less than the reservoir pressure, the well began to flow. Hydrocarbon flow into the well from the reservoir was not detected by the rig crew during this time, although there were indications that it was occurring. Among the indications were the following: (*a*) the flow of fluids pumped out of the well was larger than the flow being pumped in and (*b*) the drill pipe pressure gradually increased over time after accounting for changing pump rates (see BP 2010, Figure 8, p. 93).

Summary Finding 2.2: **The decision to proceed to displacement of the drilling mud by seawater was made despite a failure to demonstrate the integrity of the cement job even after multiple negative pressure tests. This was but one of a series of questionable decisions in the days preceding the blowout that had the effect of reducing the margins of safety and that evidenced a lack of safety-driven decision making.[4]**

Approach Chosen to Complete the Well and
Prepare for Temporary Abandonment

According to the BP accident investigation report (BP 2010), the final open hole section of the well contained several reservoirs with decreasing pore pressure with depth. As shown in Figure 2-4, the largest pore pressure was estimated at 14.1 ppg in a salt water–bearing reservoir, and the lowest was estimated at 12.6 ppg in the hydrocarbon-bearing reservoir. The largest pore pressure required that the mud weight be at least this high to prevent salt water flow from the reservoir. The fracture mud weight was just above 14.2 ppg, as evidenced by lost circulation at 18,260 feet (see BP 2010, 17–18, and Figure 2-3). This caused the margin of safety between the equivalent circulating density (ECD),[5] shown in Figure 2-3 as an equivalent mud weight, and the fracture mud weight to be very small. The operations associated with pumping cement into the annulus without fracturing one of the lower-pressure reservoirs were therefore difficult.

The completion approach chosen was to cement the production casing by using primarily foamed cement with a density low enough that the fracture pressure in the well was not exceeded. The placement of cement is always a potentially problematic operation, and if it is unsuccessful it can leave channels or pathways for fluid movement outside the casing. If the fracture pressure is exceeded while the cement is pumped, all or part of the cement can be lost to the fracture, greatly reducing the volume of cement available to isolate the well from high-pressure reservoirs. As explained below, foamed cement is more difficult to mix and place at the bottom of a well than is un-foamed cement. The foamed cement does not establish the strength of the base cement used to mix the foam, which can increase the potential for cement cracking. Furthermore, cementing hardware, such as the backflow valves used in the float collar or centralizers on the outside of the casing, is subject to failure. Hardware failure can lead to flow pathways through the cement and into the casing.

---

[4]Various questionable decisions are discussed in this chapter. Also see discussions in BOEMRE (2011), Chief Counsel (2011), DHSG (2011), and Presidential Commission (2011).

[5]ECD is a parameter that reflects the pressure that a column of fluid exerts when it is circulating. It is a function of the density of the fluid and the friction pressure in the annulus required to circulate.

Summary Finding 2.3: **The reservoir formation, encompassing multiple zones of varying pore pressures and fracture gradients, posed significant challenges to isolation using casing and cement. The approach chosen for well completion failed to provide adequate margins of safety and led to multiple potential failure mechanisms.**

Pumping Sequence of Cement Slurries for the Macondo Well

The primary function of cement is to provide the first barrier to flow from the formations into the wellbore or to flow between individual formations exposed in the wellbore. In addition, the cement stabilizes the wellbore wall and supports the steel casing. Cement slurries are often heavy, with densities around 16.4 ppg. Use of a high-density slurry is not a problem so long as the density of the slurry, along with the density of the mud, does not create a pressure in the well that exceeds the fracture pressure of exposed reservoirs. Cement slurries that are dense have a high fraction of cement in the mixture and develop excellent strength over fairly short intervals of time. This type of slurry can be adjusted by using a variety of additives to perform at the conditions found at the bottom of a given well.

For the Macondo well, the concern was to use a combination of cements with an average density sufficiently low that the open well would not be hydraulically fractured. As indicated by the experience during drilling, the density that would cause a fracture was about 14.3 ppg.

The pumping sequence of fluids for cementing the Macondo well was designed as follows to reduce the ECD during the cementing job to prevent a hydraulic fracture from being created:

1. 7 bbl of 6.7-ppg oil,
2. 72 bbl of 14.3-ppg spacer,
3. 5.26 bbl of Class H cement mixed at 16 74 ppg,
4. 47.75 bbl of N2–Class H foam cement with bottom hole density of 14.5 ppg,
5. 6.93 bbl of Class H cement at 16.74 ppg,
6. 20 bbl of 14.3-ppg spacer, and
7. 857 bbl of 14.1-ppg mud displacement (calculated).

The first four fluids were to be pumped down into the casing and up into the annulus. Fluid 5 was to be left in the shoe track. Fluids 6 and 7 were to displace the leading fluids to the float collar[6] (see Figure 2-5). The end of the casing was to be at 18,304 feet, measured from the rig floor.

---

[6]The bottom section of the casing in the Macondo well, called the "shoe track," was a section of casing about 189 feet long with a reamer-guide shoe at the bottom and a dual-flapper float collar on top.

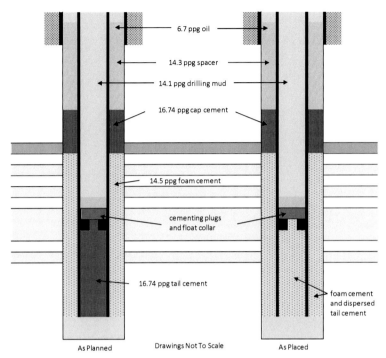

FIGURE 2-5 Planned cement location and likely cement location after pumping. Source: Committee.

To make a foamed cement slurry that has a density of 14.5 ppg at the bottom of the well, the foam quality[7] had to be 17.4 percent at bottom hole conditions of 245°F and 13,321 psi (see Appendix D for the calculations).[8] At the surface, where the conditions in the mixer were about 600 psi and 60°F, the foam quality had to be 66 percent, producing a foamed slurry of about 6 ppg, to allow for the substantial compression and heating that were to occur as the foam was pumped to the bottom of the well. (For reference, freshwater has a density of 8.33 ppg.) Figure 2-6 shows the calculated foam density versus depth.

The purpose of the float collar is to stop wiper plugs from falling farther down the casing string and to prevent cement slurry pumped into the annular space around the casing from flowing up the casing.

[7]Foam quality is the volume fraction of gas in a given volume of foam expressed as a percent.

[8]There is some discrepancy as to what the bottom hole temperature might have been when the cement was placed (circulating temperature). In this analysis, however, sufficient time is assumed to have elapsed such that the wellbore had returned to the static temperature.

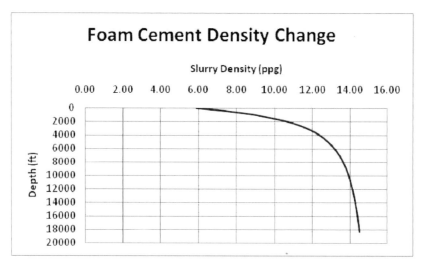

FIGURE 2-6 Calculated foam density versus depth during pumping. Source: Committee.

Once mixed, the foam was immediately pumped into the well, where pressure and temperature increased with depth, changing the foam quality and slurry density all the while. The shear associated with fluid movement down the inside of the pipe would act to break up large bubbles, which immediately reform as smaller bubbles so long as agitation is taking place.

The last of the cement (tail cement) was to be un-foamed Class H plus retarder and other standard additives. This slurry was mixed at a density of 16.74 ppg and was intended to remain inside the shoe track. As such it was meant to provide a high-quality, high-compressive-strength flow barrier inside the shoe track at the bottom of the casing. When this slurry was pumped, it was immediately on top of and in contact with the 66 percent quality foam cement that had a density of about 6 ppg near the surface. The heavier slurry, being on top of the foam cement slurry, was gravitationally unstable and thus could have fallen into the lighter foam. The tail cement might have fallen all the way through the foam, unless it was stopped by viscous forces, or it might have mixed with the foam and changed the quality of the foamed cement. In either event, the tail cement slurry remaining inside the shoe track at the end of pumping would be dispersed in the foam and would not retain its intended composition; that is, there would be no concentration of dense tail cement inside the casing as originally planned (see Figure 2-5, right side).

Finding 2.4: **The sequence of fluids used to cement the Macondo well included a low-density foamed slurry followed by a dense un-foamed tail slurry. The foam cement was designed to have a density of 14.5 ppg at the bottom of the well, but at the surface, where the foam was** mixed, the density was extremely light at around 6 ppg. The tail slurry had a density of 16.7 ppg. Because of the extreme density imbalance, the heavy tail cement on top of the foamed cement would have been gravitationally unstable near the surface, and it probably fell into and perhaps through the foamed slurry. This would have had the unintended effect of leaving a tail slurry containing foamed cement in the shoe track at the bottom of the casing rather than leaving the heavy, un-foamed tail cement.

Compressive Strength of Foamed Cement and Un-foamed Cement

The properties of Class H cement are well known. The properties of foamed cement are not well known and not easy to measure because of the compressibility of the foam. In principle, the compressive strength of foamed cement should be less than the compressive strength of un-foamed Class H cement, given the same curing conditions and additives. Testing has shown this to be true. The compressive strength of foamed cement has been shown to be approximately 35 percent of that of Class H base cement under the same curing conditions (Gardner 2010). Testing done by Chandler Engineering (Sabens and Maki 2002) has shown that foamed cement begins to establish compressive strength at about the same time as the base cement (Class H in this case), but the strength of the foam continuously lags that of the base cement as curing time increases. Accepting these trends as representative, the committee created Figure 2-7 to show the compressive strengths of the various cement slurries. The Chevron (Protocol 1) and Halliburton base slurry curves are taken from the laboratory testing done on those two un-foamed slurries.

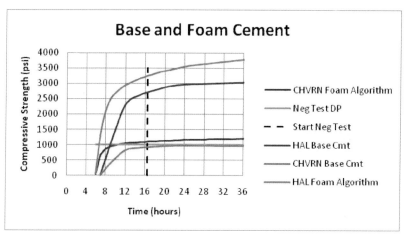

FIGURE 2-7 Uncontaminated cement compressive strength tests (DP = differential pressure). Source: Committee.

The curves for the two foamed cements are not from direct measurement but assume that the foamed cement compressive strength is reduced according to the foam protocol used in the Chevron test software (by a factor of approximately 35 percent).

The strength test results for the base slurry are all from a nondestructive compressive strength tester that measures the speed of sound through the sample as it sets. The interval transit time of sound through the sample is proportional to the compressive strength of the sample. The relationship between compressive strength and interval transit time is established by comparing the strength of samples determined by crushing tests. However, the end points of these tests were not compared with crushing tests. Therefore, the differences in the test results could be due to variation in the cement or variation in the programmed strength-to-transit-time relation.

Figure 2-7 shows the time at which the negative pressure test was started after cement slurries were pumped into the Macondo well. The figure also shows a differential pressure of about 999 psi that was created between the reservoir pressure and the reduced hydrostatic pressure inside the casing during the negative test (see Appendix D for the calculation). Figure 2-7 indicates that the foamed cement using the Chevron data would have just barely established the strength required to resist crushing under the differential pressure imposed by the negative test, assuming that the cement was not contaminated or altered by other events. The foamed cement using the Halliburton base data and the foam algorithm would not have achieved sufficient compressive strength. The positive pressure test[9] of the casing that was performed before the negative pressure test would not have affected the cement because the cement plugs within the well would have supported this increased pressure.

Another area of concern is contamination of the slurry as it is pumped into the well. The compressive strength of cement can be degraded if the slurry is contaminated by other fluids. Chevron conducted compressive strength tests of the base cement (un-foamed) with various amounts of synthetic oil-base mud contamination. On the basis of the values obtained at the critical 16.4 hour time of the negative test, the compressive strengths with mud contamination are shown in Table 2-1.

By applying the foam compressive strength algorithm mentioned above, the effect of mud contamination on base cement compressive strength was used to estimate the effect of mud contamination on the strength of foamed cement. Table 2-1 shows that as little as 5 percent mud contamination reduces the foam compressive strength to less than the 999-psi pressure differential created during the negative test. On the basis of the general relationship illustrated by the Chevron data and the assumption of the foam algorithm, if mud contamination ex-

---

[9]A positive pressure test was used to assess the integrity of the production casing and other mechanical barriers by intentionally increasing the pressure within the production casing. Because pressure inside the well remained constant during the test period, rig personnel determined that the test was successful.

ceeded 10 percent, the foamed cement would not have established sufficient strength to withstand the negative test after 48 hours of curing. Mud contamination of cement is a real possibility in the annulus if the mud is not completely removed before the cement is placed, and it is a possibility in the shoe track if any spacer flows past the top wiper plug, which is intended to separate the cement slurry from other fluids.

> *Finding 2.5:* **Foamed cement that may have been inadvertently left in the shoe track would likely not have developed the compressive strength of the un-foamed cement, nor would it have had the strength to resist crushing when the differential pressure across the cement was increased during the negative test.**

Float Collar with Flapper Valves and Differential Fill Tube

The float collar had two flapper-style backflow valves that were held open by a differential fill tube, as shown in Figure 2-8.

The differential fill tube allows mud to flow back into the casing as it is run into the well. Once the casing is in place, the differential fill tube is pumped out of the flappers and allowed to fall to the bottom of the shoe track. The flappers can then close and prevent fluids from flowing into the casing from the outside. If fluids are pumped down the inside of the casing, the flappers will open and allow fluid circulation from the inside of the casing to the outside, for example, during cementing operations. The shoe track below the float collar is made up of several joints of 7-inch casing with a ported reamer shoe[10] on the bottom.

TABLE 2-1 Chevron Data to Illustrate the Effect of Mud Contamination on Cement Compressive Strength

16.4 Hour Comprehensive Strength (psi)		
Mud %	Base Cement	Foam Algorithm
0	3,261	1,100
5	2,518	850
10	2,379	803
15	1,412	476
20	1,013	342
25	308	104

---

[10]A ported reamer shoe is a perforated piece of equipment used to guide the casing toward the center of the hole as it is lowered into the well.

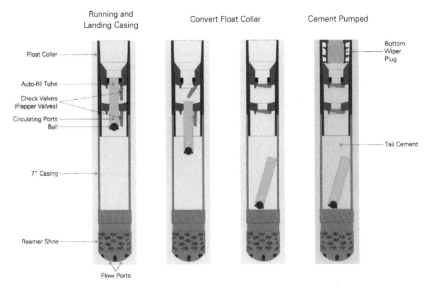

FIGURE 2-8 Float collar with flapper valves and differential fill tube. Source: BP 2010, p. 71. Reprinted with permission; copyright 2010, BP.

Once the casing was in place in the Macondo well, initial circulation could not be established until 3,142 psi of pump pressure was applied. This suggests that the shoe track was plugged with foreign material when it was run into the well. The practice of allowing mud to fill the casing by flowing up through the differential fill tube is a time-saving step that would not be needed if the casing were filled with mud from the top as it is run, a much slower process but one that reduces the possibility of debris entering the casing.

Several factors pointed to the probable failure of the flapper valves in the float collar. Once circulation was established, the pump rate never exceeded 4 barrels per minute (bpm), when at least 5 bpm was needed to shear the differential fill tube holding the flapper valves open. This indicates that the flapper valves likely remained open. Another possibility is that sufficient debris remained inside the shoe track to prevent the tube from falling out of the floats but allowing the ball to be pumped out the end of the tube. A third possibility is that the flappers in the valves were damaged when the higher pressure cleared the plug in the casing.

After the cement was pumped, spacer followed by mud was pumped. The plug bumped on the float collar after 881.5 bbl of total displacement, about what was expected, and the plug was bumped with 1,150 psi of additional pressure above the circulating pressure (BP 2010, 23). After bumping the plug, the pressure was bled off and 5 bbl of drilling mud was flowed back out of the well. The volume necessary to account for fluid compression is shown in the following equation:

$$V_c = V_m \Delta p c_m$$

where

> V_c = volume compressed (bbl);
> V_m = total volume of mud (bbl);
> Δp = applied pressure (psi); and
> c_m = mud compressibility (bbl/bbl/psi), taken from the BP report,
> Appendix R.

$$V_c = 881.5(1,150)3.3358 \times 10^{-6} = 3.4 \text{ bbl}$$

Thus, the expected flow out of the well to relieve the pressure trapped above the plug was only 3.4 bbl, and the additional 1.6 bbl that flowed out can only be attributed to flow through the flapper valves. Flow from the well ceased, and the floats were considered closed. If the valves were in fact open, the differential pressure across the flapper valves would have been very small after the trapped pressure was bled off and equalized after the small volume of flow back through the floats. The fact that more volume flowed back before flow ceased than was necessary to account for fluid compression should have been a sign— although a subtle one—that the flapper valves were likely open.

Failure of the flapper valves would have provided a possible pathway for reservoir fluids to flow inside the casing and up to the surface. Had it been suspected that the flapper valves were not closed, the well probably would have been shut in and monitored for a time sufficient for the cement to set.

Finding 2.6: **Evidence available before the blowout indicated that the flapper valves in the float collar probably failed to seal, but this evidence was not acted on at the time.**

Probable Path of Hydrocarbon Flow

Identification of the probable hydrocarbon flow path up the Macondo well can provide insights for well design considerations to enhance the safety of drilling operations. Pictures of the long string casing hanger that was recovered, shown as Figure 2-9, indicate that hydrocarbon flow was up the inside of the casing, because the inside of the hanger showed signs of fluid erosion while the outside did not. However, under the correct circumstances, flow could have been up the annulus. Because the lockdown sleeve was not installed, the margin of safety against the potential for flow up the annulus was reduced.

There are alternative possibilities for the point of entry into the casing. As discussed above, the most likely possibility appears to be the combination of weak cement inside the casing and leaking flapper valves in the float collar. Another option would be for a split to have formed in the casing at some point. A review of the casing design and the pressure to which the casing was subjected makes this possibility unlikely. In addition, the closing cementing plug was displaced to the top of the float collar with the correct volume of fluid and held pressure when the plug landed on the float collar. This would not have occurred had a split formed in the casing above the float collar.

> ***Finding 2.7:*** **On the basis of photographic evidence, it appears that flow was up the inside of the casing, because the inside of the hanger showed signs of fluid erosion while the outside did not. However, not installing a lockdown sleeve left a potential for flow up the annulus.**

Good Cementing Practice

Industry practices that have been shown to provide the best chance for quality cement jobs are based on numerous principles (Smith 1990):

• *Once casing is in the well, circulate at least one annular or one casing volume, whichever is larger.* This is done to ensure (*a*) that no debris is inside the casing that might plug the float collar or shoe and (*b*) that the open hole section is stable, has no hydrocarbon flow entering the borehole, and is free of debris before cementing. The circulation also improves the likelihood of good bonding of the cement to the surfaces of the borehole and pipe by removing stagnant mud along with any debris.

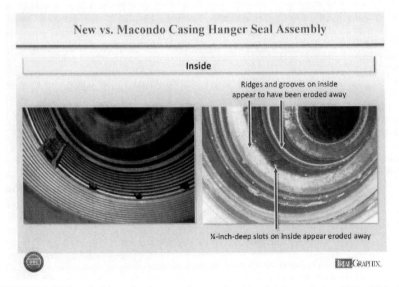

FIGURE 2-9 View inside casing hanger. Source: Presidential Commission 2010, Slide 118.

This type of circulation was not done completely at the Macondo well to reduce the possibility of exceeding the fracture pressure because of unforeseen pressure surges. This decision by BP also cut down on the time spent circulating. Failure to perform the minimum circulation could leave debris inside the casing or annulus that may plug it. Any hydrocarbons in the annulus may result in a well control problem.

- *Centralize the casing in the hole.* This helps to prevent mud-filled channels in the cement by preventing the casing from being closer to one side of the hole than another. Failure to achieve good centralization increases the likelihood that mud-filled channels will be left in the cement, which can become flow pathways. A high gas flow potential indicates that gas may percolate through the cement as it sets and provide flow pathways through the cement.

Whether the casing was adequately centralized in the Macondo well is not clear, although the final computational simulation by Halliburton suggested that a gas flow potential existed. The simulation was run to obtain an optimal number and placement of centralizers onto the production casing. The simulation was flawed in that it did not use the most accurate data set available from the well. The best practice for centralizer placement is to use the results of the simulation, if it has used the most accurate well data. Some confusion about the number and placement of the centralizers and the accuracy of the final simulation appears to have occurred. A final simulation on the basis of the most accurate well data followed by a discussion of the results to make a decision on the final centralizer placement would have been prudent.

- *Use a float collar and a guide or float shoe on the casing.* The floats are valves that prevent backflow from outside the casing.

A float collar with two float valves in it was used in the Macondo well. A reamer shoe rather than a float shoe was used so that the differential fill tube could be installed in the float collar. The use of a float shoe in addition to the float collar would have increased the redundancy and thus the margins of safety.

- *The casing should be reciprocated or rotated during the cement placement.* Casing movement tends to help keep the mud moving ahead of the spacer and cement and tends to force cement to flow into pathways that might otherwise be bypassed.

This could not be done for the Macondo well because of the design choice of using the long string of casing. The long string casing hanger must be set into the wellhead when the casing reaches bottom to avoid its becoming stuck and losing the ability to place the casing hanger into the wellhead. Once the hanger is in the wellhead, the casing cannot be moved. Had a liner been used with a rotating liner hanger, it would have been possible to rotate the casing during cementing.

- *Use a mud flush to remove the mud ahead of the cement.* Surfactants are necessary for oil-base mud to reverse wettability on casing and hole wall, and they were used.

- *Use enough cement to fill the desired hole volume plus excess to make up for hole washout and mud cake contamination.* This was probably achieved, at least to the standards of the Minerals Management Service (MMS). However, it could not be verified because cement bond logging was not used.

- *Where possible, achieve turbulent flow in the annulus, at least for the mud flush.* Turbulent flow tends to help keep the mud moving ahead of the cement. Turbulent flow probably did not occur because of the low pump rate used.

> *Finding 2.8:* **Because of the choice of the long string of production casing, it was not possible to reciprocate or rotate the casing during the cementing operation. Casing movement tends to help remove any mud left in the path of the cement and force the cement into pathways that might otherwise be bypassed. The minimum circulation of mud was not achieved in this well, which would have been helpful in removing stagnant mud and debris from the annulus. Thus, the possibility of mud-filled channels or poor cement bonding existed.**

Cement Bond Log

Whether to run a cement bond log was up to the discretion of the operator because MMS rules did not require a bond log if no lost circulation occurred during cementing operations. The decision was made not to run a cement bond log because no lost circulation had been noted during cementing operations. The design of the well placed the top of the float collar above the bottom of the deepest reservoir, so even had a log been run it could not have been run deep enough to examine the condition of the cement across all of the productive zones. The top of the cement and the cement quality in the annulus above the float collar could have been determined if the software necessary to evaluate the foam cement was on board.

> *Finding 2.9:* **No cement bond log was run to investigate the condition of the cement. The well design placed the float collar above the bottom of the deepest reservoir and would have prevented the log from investigating the lower sections of the well in which cement had been pumped.**

Onshore Oversight

No person in authority (from BP onshore management or a regulatory agency) was required to review critical test data such as the results of the negative test. Had this been a requirement before operations could continue, the negative pressure test data might have been questioned and additional testing conducted that would have exposed the problem of reservoir communication with the well. The real-time data from the rig were being recorded but not monitored on shore. Even with the negative test having been accepted, subsequent data showing that the reservoir and well were in communication might have been discovered by personnel on shore in time to take the appropriate control action.

Finding 2.10: **Although data were being transmitted to shore, it appears that no one in authority (from BP onshore management or a regulatory agency) was required to examine test results and other critical data and render an opinion to the personnel on the rig before operations could continue.**

OBSERVATIONS

Alternative Well Completion Techniques for Temporary Abandonment

Alternative cement types or completion styles were available for use at the Macondo well. When personnel on the rig encountered a low margin of safety between the ECD and the fracture pressure, the safest approach would have been to plug the bottom open portion of the well and use the geologic data to design a replacement well. The replacement could have been a new well entirely or a sidetrack out of the lower portion of the existing well. Had a higher margin of safety between the ECD and the fracture pressure been required, this is the option that most likely would have been chosen. A redesign of the completion could also have provided sufficient depth below the producing formations so that the cement bond log could examine the presence and quality of the cement throughout the productive interval.

A sufficient margin of safety should be used for the ECD while fluids are circulating so that even with unforeseen pressure surges or rate and fluid property fluctuations, the possibility of fracturing is reduced. This is especially important during cement jobs in which only small cement volumes are used because the entire cement volume could be lost to a fracture.

ECD is a function of the density of the fluids and the friction pressure in the annulus required to circulate. Thus, the fluid properties, pipe-to-hole dimensions, and pump rate have an influence. There are no standards for this margin of safety, but one possible standard is to use a safety (kick) margin of 0.5 ppg, as referenced by several authors (Bourgoyne et al. 1991; Aadnoy et al. 2009). The authors define that safety margin in the same manner as an ECD margin of safety is defined in this report: as the difference between the mud weight that would create a fracture and the ECD used. The ECD margin of safety discussed here does not obviate the need for other good drilling and completion practices to help avoid a kick or blowout.

> ***Summary Observation 2.1:*** **While the geologic conditions encountered in the Macondo well posed challenges to the drilling team, alternative completion techniques and operational processes were available that could have been used to prepare the well safely for temporary abandonment.**

Missed Opportunity to Discover Hydrocarbon Flow

Data presented in the BP accident investigation report (BP 2010, 93) indicate that drill pipe pressure increased to 1,400 psi during the last of the negative pressure tests. The increase in the drill pipe pressure at that time should have been a clear indication that hydrocarbons might be flowing into the well. The rig personnel explained the pressure increase by using an erroneous theory termed the "bladder effect."

> ***Observation 2.2:*** **Had an attempt been made to bleed off the drill pipe pressure at the end of the negative test, the communication with the reservoir would likely have been discovered.**

Instability of the Foamed Cement

Foam is inherently unstable, and the extent to which it is stable is sensitive to its chemical makeup and the environment to which it is exposed. To make a foamed cement slurry that has a density of 14.5 ppg at the bottom of the well, the foam quality must be 17.4 percent at bottom hole conditions of 245°F and 13,321 psi. At the surface, where the conditions in the mixer are about 600 psi and 60°F, the foam quality must be 66 percent, producing a foam of about 6 ppg, to allow for the substantial compression and heating that will occur as the foam is pumped to the bottom of the well.

As foam is pumped into the well, where pressure and temperature increase with depth, the foam quality and slurry density change all the while (see discussion earlier in the chapter). Also, the shear associated with fluid movement down the inside of the pipe would act to break up large bubbles, which immediately reform as smaller bubbles so long as agitation is taking place. The foam cannot be considered stable in all of these conditions.

However, a chemical blend and surfactants were used on the rig in an attempt to make the foam stable at bottom hole conditions of the Macondo well—at least long enough for the slurry to set.

After the blowout, static tests were performed under laboratory conditions on a foam cement slurry similar to the one pumped into the Macondo well. Analysts observed settling of cement and breakout of nitrogen from the foamed cement exposed to atmospheric pressure. The tests were not carried out at bottom hole conditions. Therefore, it is impossible to say whether the foam was stable at the bottom of the well.

> *Observation 2.3:* **The results of a variety of static tests of foamed cement mixed at 14.5 ppg and exposed to atmospheric pressure call into question the stability of the foam, because settling of cement and breakout of nitrogen were observed in these tests. The tests were not performed at conditions that existed during pumping or at the bottom of the well and therefore cannot be considered as representative of the foam during displacement or at bottom hole conditions.**

Potential for Cement Contamination

The lead slurry pumped into the Macondo well was made up of 5.26 bbl of un-foamed Class H cement and was in contact with the spacer and any mud that was not successfully moved out of the annulus once it was pumped out the end of the casing. The small volume of lead cement was designed to provide a high-strength cap between the spacer and mud that was ahead of and above the slurry and the foamed cement that was following and below. The small volume of lead cement may have been contaminated by either the spacer or the drilling mud from the annulus above the lead slurry or by mixing with the trailing foam slurry. Any contamination of the lead slurry would reduce the compressive strength of the cement once it set.

> *Observation 2.4:* **The pumping sequence of cement slurries and other fluids used for cementing the Macondo well subjected the volume of the lead cement slurry to contamination by the spacer or mud that was placed ahead of it. If it was heavily contaminated, the slurry would not have established a cement cap with the compressive strength of uncontaminated cement.**

Possible Path of the Blowout and Implications for Well Construction

Had the blowout occurred up the annulus rather than inside the casing, the various liner tops and the rupture discs in the 16-inch liner would have been exposed to high pressure. A liner top or the rupture discs could have failed and allowed flow to exit the annulus and flow into a formation outside the well. This would have resulted in a downhole blowout rather than the surface blowout that occurred. The shallowest possible escape point would have been 7,937 feet had a rupture disc and the top of the 18-inch liner failed (see Figure 2-2). This is about 2,937 feet below the ocean floor. Depending on the flow rate, pressure, and formation type, flow at this point might find a pathway to the ocean floor and cause a breach outside of the well. Therefore, a more robust design from a downhole blowout point of view would be to lower the possible point of escape from the wellbore to a deeper point where eventual breaching at the seafloor is impossible or at least very unlikely. This could be done by running a deeper casing string as a long string rather than as a liner and sealing it in the wellhead.

> ***Observation 2.5:* Had the path of the blowout been up the annulus, a liner top or the rupture discs could have failed and allowed flow to escape the well into a shallow formation. This would result in a downhole blowout that could breach at the seafloor under the correct conditions. Future well construction could avoid this possibility by running one of the deeper casing strings back to the wellhead where it can be sealed. For example, in this well the 13 ⅝-inch liner could have been run back to the wellhead. This would protect the shallower liner tops and rupture discs from potential exposure to high pressure from flow up the annulus from a deeper reservoir.**

Use of the Long String Production Casing

The use of the long string of production casing has already been cited as a reason the casing could not be reciprocated or rotated during cementing operations. One alternative to using the long string is to run a production liner on the drill pipe. The liner is suspended or hung several hundred feet up inside the previous casing, in this case the 9 ⅞-inch drilling liner that had been set at 17,168 feet. Cement is then pumped though the drill pipe and liner to fill up the desired annular volume. Often cement can be circulated to the top of the liner, which may create a seal at the top of the liner. If cement cannot be or is not circulated to the top of the liner, a cement squeeze is performed at the liner top where cement is forced into the annular space between the liner and the previous casing to form a seal at the top of the liner. A liner top packer that forms a mechanical seal at the top of the liner can also be deployed to replace or supplement the cement seal. The liner top is tested with a positive and a negative test in a manner similar to the testing of the long string to demonstrate wellbore isolation from the formations outside the liner. Because of the short length of the liner, it is also possible that the differential fill tube used in the float collar could have been omitted, removing one possible failure mechanism for the float equipment.

A major difference between testing of the liner top and testing of the long string is the reduced likelihood of other operations that can confuse the interpretation of the test being carried out at the same time. In addition, should the liner top show signs of a leak, the well is still substantially full of drilling mud near the bottom of the well, and the drill pipe is in a better position, near the bottom of the well, to control the leak and begin repair operations.

> ***Observation 2.6:*** **The use of a production liner rather than the long string could have allowed for the use of a rotating liner hanger to improve the chances of good cement bonding; allowed for the use of a liner top packer to add a barrier to annular flow near the bottom of the well; allowed for the omission of the differential fill tube, which would remove a potential failure mechanism for the float collar; potentially made the negative test simpler to conduct and interpret; and configured the well to better control and repair a leak in the liner by leaving the well filled with drilling mud to a greater depth and by placing the drill pipe at a greater depth in the well during the test.**

RECOMMENDATIONS

Margins of Safety

> ***Summary Recommendation 2.1:*** **Given the critical role that margins of safety play in maintaining well control, guidelines should be established to ensure that the design approach incorporates protection against the various credible risks associated with the drilling and completion processes.**

> ***Recommendation 2.2:*** **During drilling, rig personnel should maintain a reasonable margin of safety between the ECD and the density that will cause wellbore fracturing.**

There is no standard for this margin of safety. As a guide until a reasonable standard is established, industry should design the ECD so that the difference between the ECD and the fracture mud weight is a minimum of 0.5 ppg. In the event that a sufficient margin of safety cannot be maintained, the open section of the well should be plugged and alternative drilling or completion methods used in which the required safety margin can be maintained. Additional evaluations and analyses should be performed to establish an appropriate standard for this margin of safety.

Verifying Barrier Integrity

> ***Summary Recommendation 2.3:*** **All primary cemented barriers to flow should be tested to verify quality, quantity, and location of cement. The integrity of primary mechanical barriers (such as the float**

equipment, liner tops, and wellhead seals) should be verified by using the best available test procedures. All tests should have established procedures and predefined criteria for acceptable performance and should be subject to independent, near-real-time review by a competent authority.

This includes the timing of the start and the magnitude of the pressure tests compared with the amount of time needed for strength development of the cement, the results of the pressure tests, verification that the flapper valves have closed and the other mechanical seals are holding, and evaluation of cement bond logs.

Well Design Review

Recommendation 2.4: **The general well design should include the review of fitness of components for the intended use and be made a part of the well approval process.**

For example, the review should consider alternatives to the use of a series of two cement slurries that will be gravitationally unstable during placement in the well and potentially result in a slurry that does not achieve the desired compressive strength. The review should also consider the use of a differential fill device because the use of this device in the Macondo well appears to have contributed to the failure of the flapper valves to perform their intended function.

Well Construction Practice

Recommendation 2.5: **Generally accepted good operational or best practices should be used in the construction of the well. Such practices would ensure that the most accurate well data are passed from the operator to the various contractors for use in simulations and design and that the results are considered by all parties before implementation.**

3

Blowout Preventer System

If hydrocarbons unexpectedly flow into the well during drilling or other operations despite the use of primary barriers in the well, the blowout preventer (BOP) system serves as a secondary means of well control (i.e., preventing undesired hydrocarbon flow from the well). During offshore drilling, the system is deployed and attached to the wellhead to seal an open wellbore, close the annular portion of the well around the drill pipe or casing, or cut through the drill pipe with steel shearing blades and then seal the well. A typical BOP system also has more routine functions such as enabling certain well pressure tests and injecting and removing fluid from the well through its "choke" and "kill" lines. This chapter discusses the basic well control function of the BOP system that was part of the *Deepwater Horizon* mobile offshore drilling unit (MODU),[1] general studies of BOP system reliability, the role of the BOP failure in the incident, and the results of forensic analyses of the recovered BOP system. The committee found several past studies and incident reports that documented the limitations of BOP effectiveness and reliability concerns, and they are discussed below. Unfortunately, it appears that neither industry nor the Minerals Management Service (MMS) responded to these past accidents in an appropriate manner. The chapter provides the committee's findings and observations, as well as its recommendations for improving BOP system reliability.

BOP SYSTEM FOR *DEEPWATER HORIZON*

The BOP system for *Deepwater Horizon* was a massive, 57-foot-tall, approximately 400-ton well control system located at the wellhead (DNV 2011a, I, 15). A riser pipe attached to the top of the BOP system extended to the drilling platform on the *Deepwater Horizon* to permit drilling fluids to circulate between the borehole and the rig, passing through the BOP system. The bottom of the BOP rests on top of a remotely detachable connection to the wellhead, which allows the BOP to be released after well completion.

---

[1]The term "rig" is intended to be synonymous with mobile offshore drilling unit.

The BOP system was formed from two basic structural assemblies. The lower assembly, referred to as the BOP stack, rests on the wellhead connector. The upper assembly, referred to as the lower marine riser package (LMRP), was placed through a remotely detachable connection on top of the BOP stack and had roughly the same gross dimensions as the BOP stack. These assemblies, and basic functional components discussed below, are shown schematically in Figure 3-1. The LMRP had two annular preventers, and the BOP stack had four principal sealing elements: one blind shear ram (BSR) and three variable bore rams (VBRs). It also had a casing shear ram (CSR) that could shear drill pipe and casing but was not designed to seal the well. In addition, various control systems were located on the BOP system. In the event of an emergency disconnect, the LMRP was supposed to separate from the BOP stack, and the rig, riser, and LMRP were to move away from the well, which was to have been sealed by that point by the BSR in the BOP stack.

Annular Preventers

The LMRP contained two well-sealing components: the upper annular preventer and the lower annular preventer. The preventers were, as the name implies, annular in shape, and they were essentially flexible, elastomeric "doughnut" seals backed by steel elements that could accommodate a range of diameters of pipe and seal the annular space between the drill pipe and the LMRP. The annular seals were used so that the well could be tested, for example, for the so-called "negative test" discussed in Chapter 2, or potentially to stop any unwanted flow up or down the annulus.

In a blowout-prevention situation, the annular seals (if intact) could be activated and seal off the annular space between the pipe and the LMRP, although a blowout could still occur as a result of flow through the drill pipe itself if the drill pipe was not sealed.

A limiting factor was the maximum allowable differential pressure across the annular preventers. Reportedly, the upper annular preventer was designed for up to 10,000-psi differential pressure for sealing against a drill pipe or 5,000 psi when sealing the entire hole. The lower annular preventer was apparently designed for a 5,000-psi differential pressure for sealing around a drill pipe (BP 2010; Transocean 2011a).

Blind Shear Ram

The BSR was the uppermost of the five rams of the BOP stack and is shown for nominal operation in Figure 3-2. A BSR is like a massive metal scissors with two opposing blades that are designed to slice through the drill pipe as the blades pass by each other, as shown in Figure 3-3, and seal the well. The design intent was that, when the two blades of the "scissors" passed by each other and fully penetrated into the "side packers" on the other side, the seal across the BOP bore was to be effected and thus seal off the entire throat of the BOP. The BSR was, by design, a device of last resort in a hierarchy of well control strategies: when all else failed, the BSR was to slice the drill pipe and seal the well. Even if no drill pipe was present in the BOP system, the BSR was designed to seal the well when the "scissor blades" passed by each other and into the side packers.

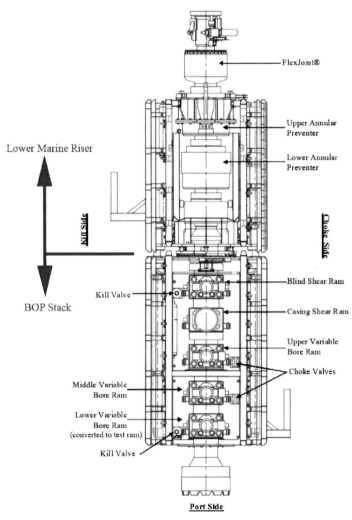

Deepwater Horizon BOP Port Side
(from DNV report of 20 March 2011, pg. 14)

FIGURE 3-1 *Deepwater Horizon* BOP port side. Source: DNV 2011a, I, p. 14. Reprinted with permission; copyright 2011, DNV.

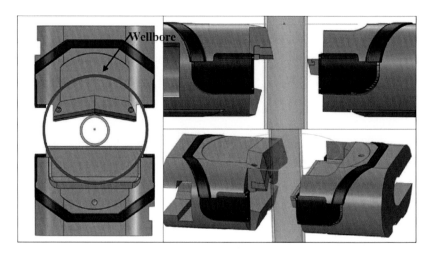

FIGURE 3-2 Sketch of intended nominal operation of BSR in the Macondo well. Source: DNV 2011a, I, p. 155. Reprinted with permission; copyright 2011, DNV.

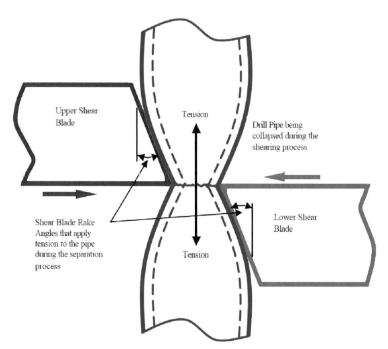

FIGURE 3-3 Upper and lower shear blades crushing the drill pipe and beginning the shearing (or breaking) operation. Source: West Engineering Services, Inc. 2004, p. 2-2. Reprinted with permission; copyright 2004, West Engineering Services, Inc.

The BSR was designed to be capable of activation in several ways (DNV 2001la, I, 2):

• By personnel on the *Deepwater Horizon* directly via either one of two control panels;
• Through the activation of the emergency disconnect system (EDS, with options EDS 1 and EDS 2) (BOEMRE 2011, 133), which was to function via either of the two control panels on the rig (the EDS was meant to be triggered when the drilling rig was to come off the well in an emergency for whatever reason);
• By the circuits located on either of two pods on the BOP system if the automatic mode function (AMF) was activated by loss of communications and hydraulic connection with the rig;
• By the autoshear function located on the BOP stack if the connection to the LMRP was physically broken; and
• By a subsea remotely operated vehicle (ROV).

The BSR is the only ram on the BOP that has automatic modes of operation: the AMF mode, which depends on the blue and the yellow pods, and autoshear mode, which does not depend on the control pods. All the other rams on the BOP are manually activated through the control pods.

Casing Shear Ram

The CSR was located below the BSR. It consisted of two pieces of metal with opposed V-shaped cutting tools above and below the plane of the slice. The CSR was designed to cut larger, thicker pipe than the BSR was designed to cut, such as casing rather than drill pipe. But the CSR, unlike the BSR, was not designed to seal off the BOP; it was designed only to cut pipe or casing.

Variable Bore Rams

Three VBRs were located near the base of the BOP stack, below the BSR and CSR. These rams had metal-reinforced elastomeric annular elements that, similar in function to the annular preventers in the LMRP, were designed to seal off the annular space between the drill pipe and the BOP system. The VBRs were more structurally robust than the annular preventers but were to close on only a narrow range of pipe diameters. The bottom VBR had been reversed to create a "test ram" that would seal against pressure in the riser instead of pressure in the well.

Control System

A number of components of the BOP control system were located on the BOP system itself, and the remainder were on the *Deepwater Horizon*. Two electrohydraulic systems, termed blue and yellow "control pods," which were housed on the LMRP, were key system control components on the BOP.

The control pods each contained electronic control units, which were connected to the drill rig with multiplexer (MUX) communication cables. A hydraulic line from the drill rig to the LMRP enabled the pressurization of the cylinder bank on the BOP system that held pressurized hydraulic fluid. The electronic control system opened and closed valves that allowed the pressurized hydraulic fluid to flow and to activate all rams and the seals in the upper and lower annular preventers.

The annular preventers and shear rams were driven by high-pressure hydraulic fluid that could have come from the rig, or—if connection with the rig was lost—from eight pressurized 80-gallon hydraulic accumulators on the BOP system. The accumulators contained high-pressure gas that was intended to push on the elastomeric bladders storing the hydraulic fluid. The high-pressure fluid initially pumped into the accumulators "charged" these accumulators. Electronic devices, when commanded, opened solenoid-driven valves that enabled the high-pressure hydraulic fluid to exit (driven by the gas in the accumulators). The high-pressure hydraulic pressure drove the rams (pistons) that displaced the preventers and rams. The electronic systems were complex and permitted control from the drilling rig, or—if communications were lost—were designed to self-initiate automated actions such as operation of the BSR.

Comments on Emergency Operations

The BSR is designed to be the true emergency sealing ram—it is the only one of the various rams on the BOP system that is designed to cut the pipe and seal the BOP system and hence the well. Sealing off the BOP system after slicing the drill pipe is a technical challenge but is well within the capabilities of current technology. The differential pressure above and below the BSR, if it works and seals, can be immense—thousands of pounds per square inch—creating enormous force and the need for high structural integrity, carefully engineered seals, and adequate testing under extreme conditions. After the metal pipe is sliced, fugitive metal from the sliced drill string cannot be permitted to become wedged between the slicing elements, which would prevent the slicing devices from fully closing and effecting a seal.

Further complicating the ram design envelope is the fact that the drill pipe joints ("tool joints") are necessarily thicker than the drill pipe itself to accommodate geometrically the threaded portions of connecting drill pipe and to transmit the drilling torque between them. Transocean's 2008 document *Well Control Complications/Emergency* provides background on the intended function of the BSRs. The Transocean document notes that "most BSRs are designed to shear effectively only on the body of the drill pipe. Procedures for use of BSRs must therefore ensure that there is no tool joint opposite the ram prior to drilling" (Transocean 2008, 2). Time and care are needed to ensure that no tool joint is located in the plane of the BSR. Furthermore, the BOP system did not contain monitoring devices that would directly indicate the location of tool joints within the BOP system to the crew on the rig. Thus, to ensure that a tool joint is not present in the plane of the BSR, the drilling crew would have to position a tool joint at a known location, either by measurement and calculation of the tool joint positions or by "hanging" a tool joint on an underlying VBR.

The 2008 Transocean document does not address determination of tool joint location during time-critical situations. The documents states that "optimum shearing characteristics are obtained when the pipe is stationary and under tension" (Transocean 2008, 2). By analogy, cutting a string or cord with scissors is always easier if the string or cord is taut. But unlike regular string, drill pipe can transmit high compressive loads, particularly when it can use the side walls of the BOP for lateral stability. In the case of the *Deepwater Horizon* on April 20, 2010, the drill string above the BOP had a "dry weight"[2] of more than 150,000 pounds.[3] If an attempt is made to shear a drill string in compression, additional friction can be substantial. When a BSR is slicing the pipe, the slice is much easier to facilitate when the pipe is in tension (being pulled) rather than under compression. Under tension, the two pieces being cut are being pulled apart, away from the cut. If, instead, the drill pipe is in significant compression, the two pieces being cut are pressed against one another and pressing on the shearing blades, making the required shearing force much higher. Furthermore, under tension, the cut pipe would be pulled away from the rams, clearing the way for the rams to seal. Under compression, the pipe would tend to be jammed into the rams and therefore block full sealing. To keep the long slender drill pipe string in tension, it is hung off a "hook" that is attached to a "traveling block" whose vertical location can be moved up and down by a huge cable hoist in the drilling derrick. At the time of the explosion on the *Deepwater Horizon*, the dry weight of the entire drill string was 217,000 pounds, entirely borne by the hook and traveling block, and the total hook load hovered around 360,000 pounds (BP 2010, 105). Witness statements indicate in the case of the *Deepwater Horizon* that the rig's traveling block, which carries the hook load (weight of the drill pipe string and upper works), fell at 22:20 (Transocean 2011a, I, 31), although the hook load itself could have been lost earlier as a result of damage from the explosions.

The design of the BOP system for the *Deepwater Horizon* focused on the use of the BSR under controlled conditions when tension in the drill pipe can be assured, and this appears to be the only way that BOP shear rams are tested. Tension would be lost, for example, if the drill pipe and the drill rig became disconnected because of an accident or explosion and the drill pipe moved downward into the well. Tension might be assured under carefully controlled

---

[2]The actual compressive load of this string at the BOP is slightly less due to the "buoyancy" of the steel relative to the weight of the fluids in the string, but not greatly.

[3]Transocean (2011a, I, 89), assuming 4,103 feet of $6\frac{5}{8}$-inch string at 32.67 pounds per foot and 900 feet of $5\frac{1}{2}$-inch string at 21.9 pounds per foot.

conditions, but not in an emergency (such as that encountered on the *Deepwater Horizon*) or in a number of other possible situations. Furthermore, since BOP ram testing is invariably done on the surface, the effects of a huge compressive pressure differential across the ram blocks are not revealed by the tests.

Some BOP systems have two BSRs as a remedy for the problem of a tool joint being in the wrong place, which can occur with a single BSR during an emergency. "All subsea BOP stacks used for deepwater drilling should be equipped with two blind-shear rams" was the conclusion of SINTEF (Stiftelsen for Industriell og Teknisk Forskning) in a study for MMS in 2001 (Holand and Skalle 2001, 96). The practice of using a single BSR that is incapable of cutting a tool joint raises serious questions about the overall reliability of the system in an emergency. The goal of future BOP designs should be high reliability under emergency conditions. How this requirement is met need not be prescriptively specified in regulation and may or may not require multiple BSRs. Regulation should require that emergency BOP reliability be empirically demonstrated by impartial testing under the most demanding conditions that would be encountered in an emergency.

AREAS OF INVESTIGATION

The committee investigated the role that the BOP system failure played in the Macondo well–*Deepwater Horizon* disaster and identified what might be done in terms of BOP system design, operation, and maintenance to prevent such an occurrence in the future.

Prior Warnings That Existing BOP System Designs Were Inadequate

Before the Macondo well blowout, there were numerous warnings to both industry and regulators about potential failures of existing BOP systems. While the inadequacies were identified and documented in various reports commissioned over the years by industry operators and regulatory organizations alike, it appears that there was a misplaced trust by responsible government authorities and many industry leaders in the ability of the BOP to act as a fail-safe mechanism.

West Engineering Studies

West Engineering Services, Inc., conducted two studies (West Engineering Services 2002, 2004) on BOPs at the behest of MMS, now known as the Bureau of Ocean Energy Management, Regulation, and Enforcement (BOEMRE). The first, *Mini Shear Study*, apparently a preliminary study, was submitted in December 2002. The study was a review of shear ram test procedures from American Petroleum Institute (API) Specification 16A and results of shear tests performed by rig operators on seven BOP systems. Fourteen cases were examined, but only seven included testing of BOP shearing capabilities. The study made several important points:

- "This study was designed to answer the question 'Can a given rig's BOP shear the pipe to be used in a given drilling program at the most demanding condition to be expected?' This can only be demonstrated conclusively by testing."
- "Of the seven [BOPs] tested, five successfully sheared and sealed based on shop testing only. If operational considerations [increased hydrostatic pressure] of the initial drilling program were accounted for, shearing success dropped to three of six (50%)."
- "This limited data set from the latest generation of drilling rigs paints a grim picture of the probability of success when utilizing this final tool in securing a well after a well control event."
- "WEST is unaware of any regulatory requirements that state the obvious: that the BOP must be capable of shearing pipe planned for use in the current drilling program."

The West Engineering study addressed the challenge of increased hydrostatic head to the BSR but did not address the even greater challenge of a large pressure differential across the rams as they attempt to seal. The West study addressed only the likelihood of the BSR shearing the pipe, not sealing it.

The West report indicates that drill pipe of a particular weight and grade may be the only pipe that a particular BOP shear ram is capable of cutting. In addition, the shear ram is unlikely to be able to sever drill pipe tool joints or heavy wall pipe such as drill collars. This means that careful housekeeping must be maintained to ensure that the correct type of pipe is in the correct position inside the BOP stack, particularly if only one shear ram exists on the BOP stack. Also, there is no automated means of ensuring that there is no tool joint in the BSR. This has to be done by (accurate) measurement and calculation.

The second study conducted by West Engineering Services, Inc., *Shear Ram Capabilities Study*, was submitted in September 2004. It expanded on the first study with theoretical and statistical studies of shear ram data from manufacturers, a review of BOP stack configurations, and a review of known BOP failures to shear and seal. The second report amplified the conclusions and observations of the first and made several additional points:

- Section 3.2 of the report states the following: "Improved strength in drill pipe, combined with larger and heavier sizes resulting from deeper drilling, adversely affects the ability of a given ram BOP to successfully shear and seal the pipe in use. WEST is currently aware of several failures to shear when conducting shear tests using the drill pipe that was to be used in the well. Only half of the operators accepting a new-build rig chose to require a shear ram test during commissioning or acceptance. This grim snapshot illustrates the lack of pre-paredness in the industry to shear and seal a well with the last line of defense against a blowout."

- The report reviewed one notable BOP "failure to shear and seal a well," the Pemex blowout in the Bay of Campeche in 1979, which released 3.3 million barrels of oil before the well was killed. The report states the following: "Reportedly they were pulling the drill string too quickly without proper fluid placement and the well started coming in. They had no choice but to close the shear rams; unfortunately, drill collars were in the stack and shearing failed" (West Engineering Services 2004, 3-4). (Note: Drill collars are thick pieces of pipe used to provide weight and stiffness at the bottom of the drill string. The tool joint for the 6⅝-inch drill pipe had an outer diameter of 8.25 inches and an inner diameter of 4.625 inches at the upset for a wall thickness of 1.8125 inches. The drill collar would normally be thicker than this. For example, an 8¾-inch outer diameter drill collar could have an inner diameter around 3.25 inches for a wall thickness of 2.75 inches.)

- The method used by several BOP manufacturers for predicting whether the shear rams will successfully shear pipe and seal the well should be more accurate. Currently only tests can demonstrate the reliability of a shear ram with the particular pipe being used. The September 2004 study called on indus-try to develop better predictive methods and to establish a database that can be shared by all.

- In the cutting process, the shear rams collapse or mash the pipe, and as the pipe is crushed, the blade angle pulls the metal into tension and breaks it in a tensile mode of failure (Figure 3-3). Depending on the ram blade design, the blade can flatten the pipe to a great extent, which in turn can prevent the ram from closing completely and sealing even if the pipe is centered.

- CSRs were introduced to shear large-diameter, thick-walled pipe such as casing. These rams do not have a sealing mechanism so that the blade can be made strong enough to shear the thicker wall pipe. CSRs are installed in the BOP stack below the BSR so that the casing rams can be used to sever thicker pipe, and then the drill string above the casing rams can be raised out of the way so that the BSR can be closed and the well sealed. Some BOP stacks use a second BSR below the CSR to create a second opportunity to shear and seal the well, which basically ensures that at least one BSR will not have a drill pipe tool joint in front of it. However, in this situation, if the severed pipe cannot be removed from the BSR area it will likely not close sufficiently to seal.

- The various control systems on the rig are not integrated. Information from the BOP system is shown as indicator lights on the control panel on the rig, but no communication is made to the pipe-handling system to ensure that the pipe is in the correct position within the BOP system for well control operations.

- The second study also illustrated the challenge of keeping long-lived BSR designs from becoming obsolete. West stated: "There are two basic types of sealing shear ram designs: single [the type in the BSR of the *Deepwater Hori-*

zon] and double 'V' blades—rams with double 'V' blades appear to have 15% to 20% lower shear forces than single blade designs. The data received primarily included shear rams having both blades 'V' shaped.[4] The two data points from shear rams that did not have both blades 'V' shaped [as was the case on the *Deepwater Horizon*] were excluded from statistical consideration" (West Engineering Services 2004, 4-2).

When a signal is sent from the drilling rig to the BOP (on the seafloor) to execute a command, the BOP sends a message back that the signal has been received. However, there are no devices to send a signal that any command has been executed, such as pressure or displacement sensors confirming that hydraulics were actuated or that rams have moved or that pipe has been cut, nor are there any flow sensors measuring whether the well has been sealed.

Additional conclusions can be drawn from the two West Engineering studies. Clearly, the operating success of the BSR was recognized to be much less than 100 percent years before the Macondo well blowout. It appears to be no better than 50 percent, on the basis of the results of the *Mini Shear Study* described above. This success ratio is inconsistent with the expectations placed on the BOP system as a fail-safe mechanism to close an out-of-control well. If well pressure is assumed to be contained by the annular preventer (assume the maximum rating of the annular preventer to represent this pressure) and if the well pressure differential across the BOP is assumed to be much larger than the hydrostatic pressure exerted by the drilling mud (as was the case in the Macondo well by at least two times), the shear success percentage demonstrated by the first study would decrease even further.

At no time is the drill pipe placed in compression during the tests discussed in the first West Engineering study. In fact, care is taken "to prevent excessive bending of the pipe" (API Specification 16A, Part B4.3.d [1997] (as cited in West Engineering Services 2004, 9-1)). The pipe section below the shear ram is not confined and is free to fall out of the shearing ram during operation. In contrast to this ideal test situation, if the pipe is in compression it may buckle as soon as the ram begins to shear it. The shear ram may not be able to cut the pipe in this condition. If the pipe is cut but cannot move out of the area of the closing rams, the rams may not seal. Sealing was not even considered in the study.

The careful housekeeping necessary to ensure that the correct type of pipe is in the correct position in the BOP stack may be difficult to accomplish in a well control emergency, further decreasing the chance that the shear rams will function correctly. Even with the addition of a CSR, the ability to seal the well is questionable if the pipe either above or below the CSR must be moved out of the way after the CSR cuts the pipe to allow one or more BSRs to seal the well. In a well control emergency there is no assurance, or even a likelihood, that the pipe can be moved at the appropriate moment to allow the BSR to seal. And obvi-

---

[4]See Figure 4.1 of West Engineering Services (2004).

ously, to ensure functionality, the BOP system design should accommodate pipe in compression and guarantee that sheared pieces of metal can be moved out of the way to allow the rams to seal.

On the basis of the West Engineering reports of 2002 and 2004, sufficient evidence of serious problems with the ability of the single BSR to meet expectations of functioning as a fail-safe device for closing an out-of-control well was available to industry and industry regulators. The problems identified in the reports for BOP systems with one BSR are compounded by the drill string being under compression, as exhibited during the Macondo well disaster. Neither of the West Engineering studies addressed the sealing capabilities or seal design of the BSR; they addressed only its ability to shear the drill pipe.

EQE Control System Risk Analysis

According to a risk assessment of the *Deepwater Horizon* BOP control system conducted by EQE International, a major contributor to the failure likelihood associated with the system was the selected stack configuration. "With only one shear ram available capable of sealing the well in, it is extremely difficult to remove all the single failure points from the system."[5] Specifically, (*a*) the final shuttle valve, which supplied hydraulics to the BSR, represented such a failure point and was predicted to account for 56 percent of the failure likelihood of the system to perform an emergency disconnect sequence, and (*b*) the failure of the four choke or kill valves each contributed about 5 percent of the failure likelihood of the EDS.[6]

According to the EQE assessment, the present shuttle valve design and its function, operation, and vulnerability to the single point failure need to be addressed systematically in the design and operation of a new-generation, post–*Deepwater Horizon* BOP system. EQE also indicates that overall, additional diversity and redundancy in the design would enhance reliability.

The next most important factor predicted by EQE to increase the risk for failure to disconnect was the human risk factor. The foremost requirement of declaring an emergency is a realization that the situation is in fact urgent. To reduce risk, EQE recommended that the frontline operator indicate, recognize, and be willing to initiate the appropriate actions or to switch to the standby pod following failure in the active pod. The BOP system should address human systems integration considerations. To ensure system reliability, the humans operating it must be willing and able to do their part.

---

[5]EQE International. 2002. Risk Assessment of the Deepwater Horizon Blowout Preventer (BOP) Control System. http://documents.nytimes.com/documents-on-the-oil-spill #document/p2. Most recently accessed Jan. 13, 2012.

[6]EQE International. 2002. Risk Assessment of the Deepwater Horizon Blowout Preventer (BOP) Control System. http://documents.nytimes.com/documents-on-the-oil-spill# document/p2. Most recently accessed Jan. 13, 2012.

The obvious command confusion on the bridge ultimately led to neither the master nor the offshore installation manager reaching a decision to execute the EDS until approximately 7 minutes after the first explosion. By that time, the subsea supervisor had already attempted to do so.

Limited Evolution in BOP Reliability

The BOP was originally invented by Cameron Iron Works, now Cameron International, in 1922. The BOP system used with the *Deepwater Horizon* was part of its TL series, based on the ram-type BOP design, which has matured and evolved over the years. In the absence of regulatory demand, the evolution of this expensive and long-lived piece of equipment appears to have been limited. However, advances in well-drilling technology, which have allowed for operation at greater water depths, presented a substantial challenge to the reliability of this basic BOP design. As other technological aspects of deepwater drilling continue to move forward, there is a need to improve BOP reliability.

However, several recent studies appear to suggest that BOPs can be trusted to act as a fail-safe mechanism. At a public forum convened by BOEMRE in September 2010 (5 months after the Macondo well blowout), an update on a study of subsea BOP reliability indicated that the probability of success of each BOP component tested was greater than 99 percent (Gallander 2010).[7] Also, a finding of 99 percent "reliability on demand" for the BOP was published in a 2009 study conducted by Det Norske Veritas (DNV 2010). It found that BOP reliability on demand was 99 percent on the basis of hours of downtime divided by total hours the BOP had been installed, and the probability of success in sealing the well by a BOP with two BSRs was predicted to be almost 70 percent. Those reliability estimates were inconsistent with the West (2002) predicted 50 percent rate of operating success of BSRs.

Holand and Skalle (2001) mentioned a reliability study of a subsea BOP system that it had performed in 1999. The study focused on deepwater kicks and associated BOP problems and safety availability aspects. It was based on information from 83 wells drilled in water depths ranging from 400 to more than 2,000 meters (1,312 to more than 6,562 feet) in the U.S. Gulf of Mexico outer continental shelf (OCS). The wells had been drilled with 26 rigs in 1997 and 1998. A total of 117 BOP failures and 48 well kicks were observed. This number is inconsistent with the estimates of 99 percent mentioned above. DNV's "reliability-on-demand" estimate of 99 percent does not reflect an important consideration for any crisis or panic situation: the drill pipe joints, which are nearly impossible for conventional BSRs to sever, make up 5 to 8 percent of the total pipe length. There is obviously a significant risk that a single BSR could be confronted with a tool joint and would fail to sever the pipe and seal the well-

---

[7]Information concerning the presentation was not included in the prepublication version of this report, which was issued in December 2011.

bore. The reasons might include the position of the joints relative to the BSR not being taken into consideration during activation of the BSR, the position of the joints moving because of flow and pressure from the well, or the hook on the rig holding the drill pipe dropping the load because of an explosion or mechanical failure. However, the 99 percent estimate appeared to be consistent with industry's perception before the *Deepwater Horizon* incident that BOPs are safe and reliable. DNV (2010) apparently did not consider the challenge of shearing a tool joint in its analysis of the reliability of a BOP stack with one or two BSRs.

Other BOP Failures

Certain previous BOP failures reported by MMS, such as that reported in MMS 2001-009: Investigation of Blowout and Fire, Ship Shoal Block 354, OCS-G 15312 Well A-2, September 9, 1999 (MMS 1999, 5-6), provided ample warnings of the problem with compression in the drill tubing:

> On the afternoon of September 9, 1999, while coiled tubing was being snubbed into Well A-2, it encountered an unknown obstruction that caused it to stop abruptly. Upon coming to a stop or shortly thereafter, the coiled tubing buckled and parted between the stripper assembly and the injector head resulting in the release of hydrocarbons to the atmosphere. [For coiled tubing rig up, see Attachment 2 of that report.] The pipe rams were closed and the shear rams were subsequently closed, thereby cutting the coiled tubing. The coiled tubing was then pulled back onto the coiled tubing reel. However, a section of coiled tubing remained between the shear rams and the injector head, where the original part [that is, the break in the tubing] had occurred. The blind rams were then closed but did not stop the flow of hydrocarbons because the coiled tubing stub was located across the blind rams. Attempts were then made to secure the well by closing the bottom manual valve on the BOP riser assembly, the crown (swab) valve, the surface safety valve, the bottom master valve, and the subsurface safety valve. The valves did not fully close because the coiled tubing remained below the shear rams and across the valve assemblies and the well continued to flow uncontrolled.

Role of BOP Failures on the Day of the Macondo
Well Blowout (April 20, 2010)

Several critical conditions must be met for a BOP system to be used successfully:

- The BOP elements must be maintained and functional.
- The crew must recognize the signs of an impending blowout in time to take the appropriate action.

- The pipe must be positioned correctly in the BOP stack.
- The BOP elements must be actuated under well conditions allowing their limited designs to seal.

As discussed in Chapter 2, the crew of the *Deepwater Horizon* did not recognize the signs of the impending blowout in time to take the appropriate action. Several indicators that should have alerted the crew that hydrocarbons from the reservoir were flowing into the well were missed, such as the following:

- *The continuing rebound in drill string pressure:* The drill pipe had unexplained and uninvestigated trapped pressure during the third negative test.
- *Excessive returns volume:* The volumes of fluid that flowed from the well during the negative pressure tests exceeded the volume necessary to account for fluid compressibility, and the flow out from the well exceeded the flow in during displacement of mud from the riser.
- *Several unexplained irregularities in pump pressure during and following the displacement of mud.*

To assist the reader in understanding where in the blowout sequence various parts of the BOP system were activated, a timeline of events as postulated by different involved parties in the investigation is shown in Figure 3-4. Note that different parties have ascribed different times to the same event, although the discrepancies are not significant. The committee has made no independent attempt to verify the accuracy of these claims.

The record indicates that the BOP upper annular preventer had endured hard use on the Macondo well, which may have reduced its ability to seal on the day of the disaster. The crew had used the lower annual preventer for the negative pressure test, and that finally effected a seal after having its pressure increased, but not before leaking 50 bbl of spacer that required having its pressure increased (Transocean 2011a, I, 29; BP 2010, 84). Why the upper annular was activated for the blowout and not the lower is not clear. After the March 8 "well control event" on the *Deepwater Horizon*, OpenWells records: "Stripped drill pipe through upper annular preventer from 17,146 ft. to 14,937 ft. while addressing wellbore losses" (BP 2010, 22). Thus, with a standard drill string length of 46 feet per section, approximately 48 tool joints were stripped through the upper annular while it was closed.[8] As SINTEF observed in a previous study, "But experience shows that when stripping is required as a part of the kick killing operation, this will cause that the annular is likely to fail afterwards (a failed annular preventer was observed after two of six stripping operations, described in Section 7.3.2 on page 81)" (Holand and Skalle 2001, 96). Despite the annulars having received hard use and being in need of maintenance, "the Panel

---

[8](17,146 – 14,937)/46 = 48.02.

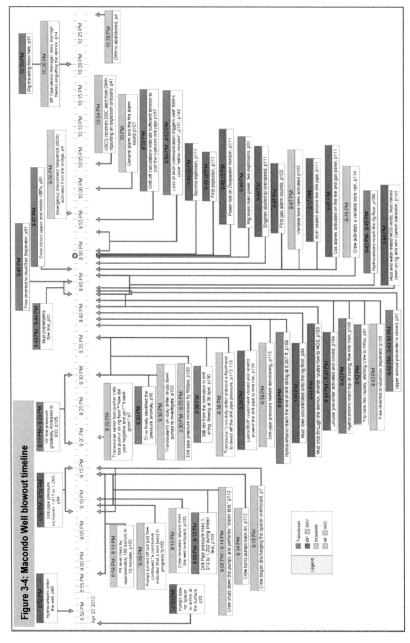

FIGURE 3-4 Macondo well blowout timeline. Source: Committee.

found that, less than a week before the blowout, BP informed Transocean that it wanted to defer maintenance to the upper and lower annulars (parts of the BOP stack)" (BOEMRE 2011, 150). In fact, BP was to confirm to Transocean that "B[P] accepts responsibility if both annulars were to fail and the stack had to be pulled to repair them."[9]

At the Marine Board of Investigation hearings in New Orleans during April 4-8, 2011, witnesses for Transocean said that it based its decisions on condition inspections and tests of functionality and that it would not be uncommon to continue a BOP service for 10 years without a major overhaul if inspections continued to show no problems. With regard to requirements for a 5-year overhaul of the BOP, Mr. Fry contended that Transocean believed it was a recommended practice in the Gulf of Mexico under API RP 53 but was not mandatory.[10]

There has been much discussion of the extent of maintenance performed on the BOP, given battery voltages and solenoid problems. Such maintenance problems are inconsistent with a device with the important role of the BOP. Different parties to the disaster have widely disparate views on what maintenance was or was not done and on what inspections, both regulatory and contractual, were or were not satisfactorily passed by the *Deepwater Horizon*. However, the fact remains that all cognizant parties—commercial, regulatory, and governmental—agreed to or permitted the *Deepwater Horizon*'s being on station drilling on April 20, 2010. Given the primitive level of status monitoring innately provided by the BOP and its controls (not even the remaining charge on critical batteries was provided), the logical consequence should have been more intense maintenance, not less. This is particularly true in view of at least some of the primitive status monitoring being an explicit choice of Transocean. "Cameron offers an option for a rig to have the ability to monitor each pod's battery voltages from any control panel. The *Deepwater Horizon* did not have this additional Cameron technology, which would have enabled the rig crew to monitor battery voltages" (BOEMRE 2011, 133).

But in the final analysis, the faulty design of the BSR, which would not shear and seal a modest 5½-inch-diameter drill string (well below its rating) in compression, significantly contributed to this national disaster. Given that there was only one BSR in the BOP system at the Macondo well and that it failed to stop the blowout because of its design and operational shortcomings, there is an urgent need for those shortcomings to be corrected.[11]

---

[9]BP-HZN-MBI00254591 in BORMRE (2011, 151).

[10]Testimony of Michael Fry, April 6, 2010, Hearing Before the *Deepwater Horizon* Joint Investigation Team, 72.

[11]To assist the reader in understanding where in the blowout sequence various parts of the BOP system were activated, a timeline of events is shown in Figure 3-4.

Forensic Analysis of the BOP

The committee reviewed the BOP forensic analysis work done on the Macondo well hardware recovered from the seafloor as part its overall evaluation of the available supporting evidence.

DNV (USA) was selected by the U.S. Coast Guard–BOEMRE Joint Investigation Team to conduct the forensic evaluation of the BOP. DNV is a risk management company providing a variety of services to the maritime and oil and gas industries, including materials testing and offshore classification. The forensic evaluations were conducted according to a test plan reviewed by a technical working group that included representatives from BP, Transocean, Cameron, the Chemical Safety Board, the U.S. Department of Justice, and the Multidistrict Litigation Panel and approved by the Joint Investigation Team.

The product of the DNV investigation was a final report (DNV 2011a) and the subsequent addendum (DNV 2011b). Both BP and Transocean have independently reported their earlier or additional investigations into why the BOP failed to perform as desired (BP 2010; Transocean 2011a).

The central finding of the DNV report was that the BSR blades could not shear a 5½-inch drill string and then seal against each other because the drill string was located on the side and not the center of the BOP annulus. This finding appears to be strongly supported by a wide range of corroborating physical evidence, and it has been embraced by Transocean (Transocean 2011a, I, 137). The asymmetric dents in the drill pipe sheared by the rams [impressed into steel 0.350 inch thick (DNV 2011a, I, 128)] credibly matched to the geometry of the ram blocks (DNV 2011a, I, 100) leave little room for alternative explanations. In addition, there is compelling physical evidence that the upper annular preventer above the BSR and the VBRs below the BSR were activated and closed on the drill string before the BSR was activated, centering the drill string in the BOP annulus in close proximity to the BSR. Thus, the DNV conclusion that the drill string was under significant compressive load also appears logical and perhaps the only feasible mechanism for pushing the drill string so far off center in such a short distance (27.3 feet) (DNV 2011a, I, 151). The consequence of not extending the blades on the BSR to cover the complete BOP annulus can be clearly observed in Figure 3-5. As was noted earlier, West Engineering dropped the one straight and one V-blade BSR configuration from its study in 2004 because of the higher shearing pressure this design required. It is also apparent that this configuration had less ability to center an off-center drill string than a double-V ram design would have evidenced. The gaps on the sides of the BSR blades, and their obvious inability to shear any pipe that was in this area, indicate that the possibility of pipe being off center was not considered in this design.

The source of the high compressive load on the drill string causing the "elastic buckle" (DNV 2011a, I, 150) driving it to the side of the annulus, calculated by DNV to be in excess of 113,000 pounds (DNV 2011a, I, 153), was not definitively determined. However, among a number of possible sources that it considered for this load, DNV hypothesized the following: "Forces from the flow of the well induced a buckling condition on the portion of drill pipe between the Upper Annular and Upper VBRs" (DNV 2011a, I, 174). Further complicating the determination of the compressive load source is uncertainty about exactly when the BSR was activated, since different sources of compressive drill string load are potentially available only at certain times in the failure sequence. Two distinct BSR activation times have been hypothesized by the parties involved. Transocean maintains that both the blue (Transocean 2011a, I, 159) and the yellow (Transocean 2011a, I, 158) control pods were functional and available at the time of the explosion and loss of MUX and hydraulic connection to the *Deepwater Horizon* at 21:49, and therefore the AMF was functional and functioned "within minutes" (Transocean 2011a, I, 162) on April 20. However, BP and DNV have hypothesized, on the basis of the retrieved condition of the blue pod batteries (BP 2010, 150, 153) [74 days after the explosion (Transocean 2011a, I, 159)] and the incorrectly wired Solenoid 103 on the yellow pod (BP 2010, 150), that BSR activation was more likely due to the autoshear function, which bypasses Solenoid 103 and was caused by ROV intervention at 07:30 on April 22 (Transocean 2011a, I, 162).

Transocean [2011a, I, 157 (footnote G)] argues as follows:

> The AMF system fired the HP shear circuit locking the ST Locks behind the upper and middle VBRs moments after the power was lost to the pods. If the AMF had not fired, the rams would have had to have been held closed by only the wellbore pressure for 33.5 hours until the auto-shear pin was cut by an ROV. When the auto-shear pin was cut on April 22, 2010, at 7:30 a.m., there was no indication of fluid discharge from the control pods indicating that the BSR and the ST Locks were already in the closed and locked position. If the BSR was still open, approximately 30 gallons of fluid would visibly discharge from the open side of the BSR and ST Locks.

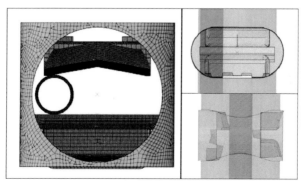

FIGURE 3-5 Finite element analysis model of BSR blade surfaces and off-center drill pipe. Source: DNV 2011b, p. 15. Reprinted with permission; copyright 2011, DNV.

But BP (2010, 156) has observed, not wholly inconsistently with Transocean's claim:

> In an effort to actuate and open the autoshear valve, the autoshear rod was cut at approximately 07:40 hours on April 21, 2010. Incident management team (IMT) responders, who were monitoring ROV operations when the autoshear was activated, reported that movement was observed on the BOP stack. This movement was consistent with stack accumulators discharging. A short time later, a leak on the ST lock hydraulic circuit, which was downstream of one of the BSR bonnet sequence valves, was observed, indicating that the lock circuit and the BSR were closed.

DNV (2011a, I, 169) independently observed:

> While the conditions necessary for AMF/Deadman existed immediately following the first explosion/loss of rig power, because of the inconsistent behavior of original Solenoid 103Y and the state of the 27V battery bank on the Blue Control Pod, it is at best questionable whether the sequence was completed.

The weight of the evidence appears to support the conclusion of BP and DNV that the BSR was activated by the autoshear, but for additional reasons not addressed in their reports. All parties appear to agree that the upper and middle VBRs successfully sealed the well a minute or two before the explosions, accounting for the large pressure spike in the drill string starting at 21:47 (BP 2010, 105). Both these VBRs were found with their ST locks set (DNV 2011a, I, 31), meaning that they stayed applied, irrespective of flow or pressure, until the BOP was retrieved. Thus, until they were eventually eroded, the annulus of the BOP remained sealed by these VBRs. During this period the only flow path for hydrocarbons from the formation to the rig was the drill string. If Transocean was correct, this flow path was interrupted "within minutes" by the AMF activating the BSR. It appears undisputed that the BSR sheared the drill string off center in the manner illustrated by Figure 3-6, which is from the DNV report addendum (DNV 2011b, 17). If Transocean is correct and the AMF functioned "within minutes" of 21:50, then the entire hydrocarbon communication with the Macondo well must have been through the small flow area that would exist at that time from the sheared end of Pipe Segment 94 (End 94B) (DNV 2011a, I, 95). Note on Figure 3-6 in Frame 23 that the sheared pipe end is shown with only 277,000 pounds of ram load applied where the BSR will ultimately apply approximately 900,000 pounds of ram force at the regulated pressure of 4,000 psi (DNV 2011a, 14). Thus, substantially less cross-sectional flow area will be available to well hydrocarbons than is shown in Frame 23.

If the AMF functioned for at least some time, there should have been a significant reduction in hydrocarbon flow from the well that would have become

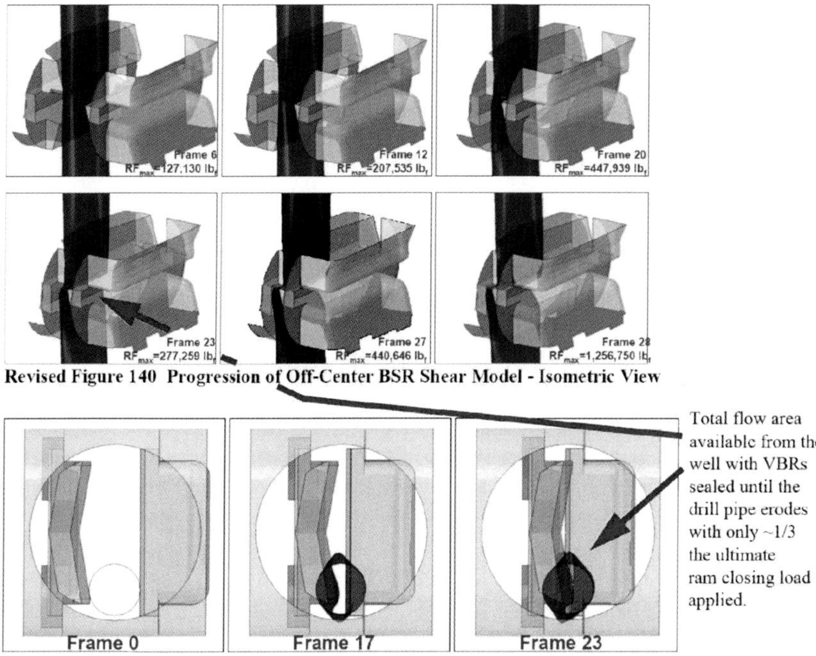
Frame 6
Frame 12
Frame 20
Frame 23
Frame 27
Frame 28
Revised Figure 140 Progression of Off-Center BSR Shear Model - Isometric View
Frame 0
Frame 17
Frame 23
Total flow area available from the well with VBRs sealed until the drill pipe erodes with only ~1/3 the ultimate ram closing load applied.

FIGURE 3-6 Progression of off-center BSR shear model, isometric view (*top*) and top view showing deformation of drill pipe outside of shearing blade surfaces (*bottom*). Source: DNV 2011b, p. 17. Reprinted with permission; copyright 2011, DNV.

apparent after the initial hydrocarbons that had leaked into the riser before the rams were activated blew out on the surface. This statement is true even if the explosions completely severed the drill string at the surface. After the drill string contents blew out, it would no longer have significant communication with the well for a period of time in the face of 900,000 pounds of clamping pressure on the output end of the severed drill string.

However, this scenario does not appear to be borne out by witness descriptions of the fire. "It was quickly apparent to the bridge team that it was impossible to regain control of the well or to fight the fires" (Transocean 2011a, I, 32). Several crew members jumped into the sea as the fire continued to grow in intensity (Transocean 2011a, I, 32). Thus, there appears to have been no interruption in flow from the well during the crucial minutes after the initial explosions, and the BSR rams appear not to have closed until the autoshear was activated.

Given the timing of the BSR activation, attention can now turn to the potential sources of the compression in the drill string that produced an off-center position in the BSR. Transocean produced several calculations consistent with the DNV hypothesis purporting to show that the pressure in the formation was sufficient to lift the drill string and create the necessary compression. The first is set forth as: "5.5-in. drill pipe = 23.75 in.^{2} × 7,000 psi = 166,250 lb. lift" (Transocean 2011a, I, 157, Footnote E). This is Transocean's assumed loading on the drill string after the VBR's activation and presumably at the time of the postulated AMF activation, "within minutes" of the explosions. While the formula is mathematically correct, its application to the Macondo well drill string is difficult to see. To start with, 1 minute before the explosions, after the VBR activation, the internal drill string pressure on the rig shot up to more than 5,600 psi (BP 2010, 105). The bottom of the 5½-inch section of the drill string reached a depth of 7,546 feet below the drill rig floor (Transocean 2011a, I, 89). On the basis of the assumption that the entire length of drill string was filled with seawater being used to displace the drilling mud, at 0.445 psi per foot the seawater added another 7,546 × 0.445 = 3,358 psi of hydrostatic head to the internal drill pipe pressure measured on the rig, for a total pressure inside the end of the 5½-inch section of drill string of approximately 5,600 psi + 3,358 psi = 8,958 psi. The pressure measured on the rig in the drill string could only increase from about 1,200 psi to about 5,600 psi in 2 minutes if the formation pressure being exerted at the tip of the drill string was greater than the drill string pressure plus the hydraulic head of the total drill string (about 5,600 psi + 3,707[12] psi), or about 9,307 psi, and flow was going into the drill string.

A different calculation of the same loading is set forth in Appendix M of Transocean (2011a): "In the shut in condition, the pressure below the VBR is 8,000 – 8,500 psi. With an assumed hydrocarbon density of 2 ppg above the VBR, the pressure above the VBR is 500 psi. Thus, the pressure drop across the VBR is about 8,000 psi, which corresponds to a net compression of about 120 kips" (Transocean 2011, Appendix M, 29). Needless to say, the two calculations do not agree.

Matters are different if it is postulated that the explosions on the rig ruptured the drill string and allowed the high drill string internal pressure to bleed down to atmospheric pressure at the rig. Such an event would leave only the 3,358 psi of hydrostatic internal pressure in the drill string, acting on the 4.8-inch internal diameter at the end of the 5½-inch section, for a total hydrostatic load of 60,765 pounds. This would be sufficient to reduce Transocean's postulated lift by almost half and Transocean's total calculated lift well below the compressive force level necessary at the BOP calculated by DNV. However, Transocean's first lift calculation also ignored the weight of the drill string below the BOP. On the basis of the data for drill string dimensions and weights (Transocean 2011a, I, 89), this is calculated as 62,232 pounds dry weight, which corrects to 53,301 pounds buoyed by seawater. Transocean's calculation in Appendix M would appear to take cognizance of the drill string weight, but neither appears to consider the pressure internal to the drill string. In both calculations Transocean treats the drill string as a piston, when in reality it is more like a straw, open at the bottom and the top after the explosions. The hydrostatic pres-

---

[12] 8,367 total feet of drill string × 0.445 psi/ft.

sure internal to the end of the 5½-inch drill string section and the buoyed weight of drill string below the BOP together produce 114,065 pounds of load. This must be overcome before the first pound of compression will be felt by the drill string in the BOP under any postulated failure scenario consistent with DNV's hypothesis. An additional 821 feet of 3½-inch tubing is attached to the end of and hanging below the 5½-inch drill string, which is included in the calculations of buoyed weight but whose hydrostatically induced internal pressure would be even greater due to an additional 821 feet of head. Since the end of the 3½-inch tubing is opened to the flow from the formation and the top of the drill string has clearly been ruptured by the explosions, the area of the 3½-inch drill string is a "straw" that cannot be used in a calculation of compression load from pressure, so it is difficult to postulate a situation, short of some incredibly high flow rates, under which a significant pressure differential could be established between the inside and the outside of the drill string. Production of 115,000 pounds of drill string compression in the BOP as postulated by DNV requires that flow friction and pressure below the BOP generate a total of almost 230,000 pounds of vertical lift. There is a total of about 3,337 feet of drill string below the BOP. For fluid drag to produce the required vertical lift would require an average of 69 pounds of vertical fluid drag per linear foot of drill string. However, it is unlikely that the drag between the 3½-inch tubing and the 5½-inch drill string would be uniform, given that the flow is predominantly up the drill string, as evidenced by the erosion wear at the VBRs, which remain applied until the BOP is recovered. While the fluid drag is likely to be significantly greater in the 3½-inch tubing than in the 5½-inch drill string, use of even the 69-pound average means that the top of the 3½-inch tubing would experience a compressive load of 56,650 pounds. Whether the walls of this 9.3-pound-per-foot tubing can transmit a compressive load of 28 tons without local wall buckling is unknown.

Given the technical challenge of developing the 115,000 pounds of vertical compressive load on the drill string postulated by DNV through flow friction, gravity is a simple and attractive alternative. Above the BOP sit approximately 134,045 pounds of 6⅞-inch drill string and 19,710 pounds of 5½-inch drill string, for a total dry weight of 153,755 pounds of drill string. Corrected for buoyancy, this results in a net drill string weight at the BOP of 135,904 pounds. This is slightly more than the 115,000 pounds postulated by DNV as necessary to produce the observed elastic buckling in the drill string. While the rig's traveling block was observed to fall about 30 minutes after the explosion, when vertical support of the drill string was lost is unknown. For the vertical mass of the drill string above the BOP to be the source of the compressive load in the BOP at the time of the application of the autoshear, the drill string must remain intact above the BOP. Transocean calculates that the drill string parted above the upper annular preventer through excessive tensile load at 21:56, approximately 6 minutes (Transocean 2011a, I, 157) after the explosions, as the powerless *Deepwater Horizon* drifted off station. Transocean's assumptions about the integrity of the derrick after the explosions and its support of the weight of the drill string are not set out.

DNV (2011a) hypothesized that the drill string "would have been set in slips to remove the suspended load from the derrick or travelling block." However, there is no available evidence of this or of how the slips would have fared in the two explosions even if they had been used. As illustrated by BP (2010, 105, Figure 17), the hook load measured the weight of the drill pipe, top drive, blocks, and so forth right up to the moment of explosion. The slips were not set. While DNV (2011a) did not consider it likely that the two VBRs applied simultaneously with full rig hydraulics still connected could have generated the gripping force necessary to support the compression, no data or tests were presented in support of this hypothesis.

FINDINGS

Summary Finding 3.1: **The loss of well control was not noted until more than 50 minutes after hydrocarbon flow from the formation started (see timeline in Figure 3-4), and attempts to regain control by using the BOP were unsuccessful. The BSR failed to sever the drill pipe and seal the well properly, and the EDS failed to separate the lower marine riser and the *Deepwater Horizon* from the well.**

The EDS failed to operate because of the loss of MUX communication in the explosion or the subsequent fire which burned for 7 minutes on the rig floor before EDS activation was attempted.

Finding 3.2: **The crew did not realize that the well was flowing until mud actually exited and was expelled out of the riser by the flow at 21:40. Early detection and control of flow from a reservoir are critical if an impending blowout is to be prevented by a BOP whose use against a full-flowing well is untested.**

Finding 3.3: **Once mud began to flow above the rig floor, the crew attempted to close the upper annular preventer of the BOP system, but it did not seal properly. The BOP system had been used in the month previously to strip 48 tool joints, and apparently it was untested for integrity afterwards. Annulars are often unable to seal properly after stripping. In addition, the flowing pressure inside the well may have been larger than the preset annular closing pressure could overcome. What tests of sealing against flow have been done on this design of annular are unknown.**

Finding 3.4: **The crew also closed the VBRs. The damaged pipe under the upper annular demonstrated its failure to seal, and the well was**

only sealed, resulting in the final pressure spike, when these VBRs were closed. The DNV investigation also found that these rams closed, and they could only be closed by command from the rig control panels and not by an ROV. At this point the flow from below the VBRs would have been closed off, but gas and oil had already flowed into the marine riser above the BOP system and continued to rise to the surface, where the gas exploded.

Finding 3.5: The internal BOP, which functions as a safety valve on the top of the drill pipe, was not closed (BP 2010, 25). Also, approximately 30 minutes after the explosion the traveling block was observed to fall and the rotary hose (used to conduct drilling fluid) could have been destroyed. The growing fire indicates that the drill pipe was broken in the initial explosion and the fall of the traveling block could have allowed even more flow to escape up the drill string. This was the likely path of hydrocarbon flow before the closure of the BSR (see Chapter 2).

Finding 3.6: Once the fire started on the rig, an attempt was made (after 7 minutes) to activate the EDS, which should have closed the BSR and disconnected the LMRP. This appears to have failed because the MUX communication cables were destroyed by the explosion or fire.

Finding 3.7: Once hydraulic and electrical connection with the rig was lost at the BOP, the AMF should have activated the BSR. It might have failed at this time because of a low battery charge in one control pod and a miswired solenoid valve in the other, but both these points are in dispute. However, no short-term reduction in hydrocarbon flow from the well was observed after the initial fire and explosion (see Figure 3-4). Such a reduction would necessarily have resulted from the VBRs sealing the annulus in the BOP and the failed BSR shearing action effectively choking, at least for a brief period of time, virtually the entire cross section of the 5½-inch drill string. Viewed in total, the evidence appears more supportive of the autoshear activation of the BSR.

Finding 3.8: The BSR appears to have been activated after 07:40 on April 22, 2010, if not earlier, when the hydraulic plunger to the autoshear valve was cut by an ROV. However, regardless of when the BSR was activated, the well continued to flow out of control.

Finding 3.9: DNV hypothesized that the drill pipe below the annular preventer was being forced upward by the pressure of the flowing well, resulting in a 115,000-pound net compressive force on the drill pipe in the BOP sufficient to buckle the drill pipe until it came in contact with the inside of the BOP system (DNV 2011a, I, 174). However, the fluid mechanics inherent in this assumption are dubious. The 135,000 pounds of buoyed drill string weight above the BOP appears to be a more plausible source of the compression.

Finding 3.10: **When it was activated, the BSR was unable to center the drill pipe in its blades and failed to cut the pipe completely. The blades of the ram were of the old straight and V combination, which has been shown to be inferior in its shearing performance to the double-V blade geometry (West Engineering Services 2004). Because the BSR blades did not fully span the BOP annular, a mashed segment of pipe was caught between the rams and prevented them from closing to the point where they could seal (DNV 2011b, 17) (see Figure 3-6).**

An alternative hypothesis for compressive loading on the drill pipe is that the loading could have occurred if the drill string were dropped from the top drive in the derrick. This equipment likely had been damaged or destroyed by an explosion and fire. A closed VBR would act to restrict the motion of the drill pipe. The drill pipe above the BOP would go into a long helical buckle above the ram and in the marine riser, placing a considerable compressive load on the drill pipe in the BOP system. On the basis of solid mechanics, a pressurized tube reacts as if it is under compressive load.

Under either of the scenarios mentioned above, the buckling force would have occurred as soon as the elements of the BOP system prevented the upward or downward motion of the drill string, and clearly there are several plausible reasons why the drill string would have been in compression.

Finding 3.11: **After the rig lost power and drifted off station, the marine riser kept the vessel tethered to the BOP system.**

Finding 3.12: **Flow from the well then exited the partially severed drill pipe in the BSR and began to erode parts of the ram and BOP stack by fluid flow.**

Finding 3.13: **After the vessel sank at 10:22 on April 22, 2010, the marine riser with the drill pipe inside was bent at a number of places, including the connector to the BOP, and oil and gas began to flow into the ocean.**

Finding 3.14: **The effect of closing the CSR on April 29, 2010, was to provide a new flow path exiting the severed drill pipe below the CSR and passing the CSR rams that were not designed to seal. Severe fluid erosion occurred past the CSR, with deep cuts made in the surrounding steel of the BOP housing itself, endangering the integrity of the housing.**

Finding 3.15: Unfortunately, even if the BSR had functioned after being activated by the EDS or the AMF, it would not likely have prevented the initial explosions, fire, and resulting loss of life, because hydrocarbons had already flowed into the marine riser above the BOP system. If the BOP system had been able to seal the well, the rig might not have sunk, and the resulting oil spill would likely have been minimized.

Summary Finding 3.16: The BOP system was neither designed nor tested for the dynamic conditions that most likely existed at the time that attempts were made to recapture well control. Furthermore, the design, test, operation, and maintenance of the BOP system were not consistent with a high-reliability, fail-safe device.

Finding 3.17: Regulations in effect before the incident required the periodic testing of the BOP system. However, they did not require testing under conditions that simulated the hydrostatic pressure at the depth of the BOP system or under the condition of pipe loading that actually occurred under dynamic flow, with the possible entrained formation rock, sand, and cement, and no such tests were run. Furthermore, because of the inadequate monitoring technology, the condition of the subsea control pods at the time of the blowout was unknown.

Finding 3.18: The committee's assessment of the available information on the capabilities and performance of the BOP system at the Macondo well points to a number of deficiencies (listed below) that are indicative of deficiencies in the design process. Past studies suggest that the shortcomings also may be present for BOP systems deployed for other deepwater drilling operations.

  1. The committee could find no evidence that the BOP design criteria or performance envelope was ever fully integrated into an overall well control system perspective, nor that BOP design was consistent with the BOP's critical role in well control.
  2. While individual subsystems of various BOP designs have been studied on an ad hoc basis over the years, the committee could find no evidence of a reliability assessment of the entire BOP system, which would have included functioning at depth under precisely the conditions of a dynamic well blowout. Furthermore, the committee could find no publicly available design criteria for BOP reliability.
  3. The entire BOP system design is characterized by a previously identified lack of redundancy:
     • There is only one BSR.
     • One shuttle valve is used by both control pods.

- Each MUX cable is incapable of monitoring the entire BOP system independently.

4.   No design consideration appears to have been given to BSR performance on pipe in compression.

5.   The BSR was not designed to shear all types and sizes of pipe that might be present in the BOP system.

6.   The BSR probably did not have the capability of shearing or sealing any pipe in significant compression.

7.   There was a lack of BOP status monitoring capabilities on the rig, including

- Battery condition,
- Condition of the solenoid valves,
- Flow velocity inside the BOP system,
- Ram position,
- Pipe and tool joint position inside the BOP system, and
- Detection of faults in the BOP system and cessation of drilling operations on that basis.

Finding 3.19: The failure of the AMF to activate might have been due to malfunctions in the control pods that could not be detected. In view of the state of the pipe in the well after the explosion, whether the BSR would have functioned properly is uncertain. This issue is moot if the rams could not perform their intended functions whenever they were activated.

Finding 3.20: The regulations did not require that the design of the equipment allow for real-time monitoring of critical features, such as the battery condition in the control pod, so that maintenance issues could be readily discovered. The current test protocol for the BSRs, for example, is designed for near-ideal surface conditions rather than the harsher conditions found on the ocean floor.

Finding 3.21: When a signal is sent from the drilling rig to the BOP (on the seafloor) to execute a command, the BOP sends a message back that the signal has been received. However, there are no transducers that detect the position or status of key components, and there are no devices to send a signal that any command has been executed (such as pressure or displacement sensors confirming that the hydraulics have been actuated, that rams have moved, or that pipe has been cut). Furthermore, there are no sensors to communicate flow or pressures in the BOP to the rig floor.

OBSERVATIONS

Observation 3.1: In the confusion of an emergency such as the one on the *Deepwater Horizon*, it is not surprising that a drill crew would not take the time to determine whether a tool joint was located in the plane of the BSR or whether tension was properly maintained in the drill pipe.

Observation 3.2: In terms of emergency procedures, such as an emergency disconnect or autoshear function of the BOP system on its own, there is no ability to manipulate the tool joint position or the level of tension or compression in the drill pipe. The BSR was not designed to work for the full range of conditions that could be realistically anticipated in an emergency.

RECOMMENDATIONS

Summary Recommendation 3.1: BOP systems should be redesigned to provide robust and reliable cutting, sealing, and separation capabilities for the drilling environment to which they are being applied and under all foreseeable operating conditions of the rig on which they are installed. Test and maintenance procedures should be established to ensure operability and reliability appropriate to their environment of application. Furthermore, advances in BOP technology should be evaluated from the perspective of overall system safety. Operator training for emergency BOP operation should be improved to the point that the full capabilities of a more reliable BOP can be competently and correctly employed when needed in the future.

Recommendation 3.2: The design capabilities of the BOP system should be improved so that the system can shear and seal all combinations of pipe under all possible conditions of load from the pipe and from the well flow, including entrained formation rock and cement, with or without human intervention. Such a system should be designed to go into the "well closed" position in the event of a system failure. This does not mean that the BOP must be capable of shearing every drill pipe at every point. It does mean that the BOP design should be such that for any drill string being used in a particular well, there will always be a shearable section of the drill pipe in front of some BSR in the BOP.

Recommendation 3.3: The performance of the design capabilities described in the preceding recommendation should be demonstrated and independently certified on a regular basis by test or other means.

Recommendation 3.4: The instrumentation on the BOP system should be improved so that the functionality and condition of the BOP can be monitored continuously.

Summary Recommendation 3.5: Instrumentation and expert system decision aids should be used to provide timely warning of loss of well control to drillers on the rig (and ideally to onshore drilling monitors as well). If the warning is inhibited or not addressed in an appropriate time interval, autonomous operation of the BSRs, EDS, general alarm, and other safety systems on the rig should occur.[13]

Recommendation 3.6: An unambiguous procedure, supported with proper instrumentation and automation, should be created for use as part of the BOP system. The operational status of the system, including battery charge and pressures, should be continuously monitored from the surface.

Recommendation 3.7: A BOP system with a critical component that is not operating properly, or one that loses redundancy in a critical component, should cause drilling operations to cease. Drilling should not resume until the BOP's emergency operation capability is fully cured.

Recommendation 3.8: A reliable and effective EDS is needed to complete the three-part objective of cutting, sealing, and separating as a true "dead man" operation when communication with the rig is lost. The operation should not depend on manual intervention from the rig, as was the case with the *Deepwater Horizon*. The components used to implement this recommendation should be monitored or tested as necessary to ensure their operation when needed.

If the consequence of losing communication and status monitoring of the BOP system is an automatic severing of the drill pipe and disconnection from the well, the quality and reliability of this communication link will improve dramatically.

Recommendation 3.9: BOP systems should be designed to be testable without concern for compromising the integrity of the system for future use.

---

[13]This recommendation is also presented in Chapter 4 as Recommendation 4.1.

4

Mobile Offshore Drilling Units

This chapter describes the basic function of the *Deepwater Horizon* mobile offshore drilling unit (MODU);[1] its application in the Macondo well exploration; and specific areas of investigation undertaken by the committee, including rig safety systems, training and responsibilities of rig personnel, and events on the rig just before and in response to the explosions and fire. Many of the issues considered were raised in witness testimony at investigative hearings, during presentations to the committee, and in previously published reports (BP 2010; BOEMRE 2011; Chief Counsel 2011; DHSG 2011; Presidential Commission 2011; Republic of the Marshall Islands 2011; Transocean 2011a; USCG 2011), especially in terms of the role of the rig and its crew in the loss of well control and loss of life. The chapter provides the committee's findings and observations on those topics, as well as recommendations for improving rig safety.

DEEPWATER HORIZON RIG

The *Deepwater Horizon* was a dynamically positioned drilling unit designed to propel itself to an exploration site and then keep station over the site (without using a fixed mooring system), acting as a base for drilling operations (see Figure 4-1). The rig served as a self-propelled vessel, a stable floating base for drilling and outfitting a deep subsea well, a command and control base for exploration, and a home for its crew.[2]

As is typical for offshore drilling rigs, when it was under way at sea, the rig was operated by a crew under the command leadership of a U.S. Coast Guard–licensed master. Crew actions were directed by the offshore installation manager (OIM) whenever the rig was attached to the bottom or made fast over a drilling site. The crew members involved in the use of offshore equipment were divided into functional areas of deck, engineering, and drilling and subsea operations, each of which was led by a department head, subordinate to the master

---

[1]The term "rig" is intended to be synonymous with MODU.

[2]See Republic of the Marshall Islands (2011) for additional overview information on the *Deepwater Horizon.*

and OIM in the command organization. Crew members stood watches in a pre-scribed rotation, and crews were regularly cycled on and off the rig to support continuous operations.

The *Deepwater Horizon* worked on the Macondo well under the command of Transocean even during drilling operations, as contracted by BP. BP's on-site direction was provided by two well site leaders. Four others from BP (a well site trainee and three subsea engineers) were also aboard. In addition, BP separately contracted for services aboard the *Deepwater Horizon* from contractors, includ-ing Halliburton (cementing), Sperry Sun (well data logging), M-I SWACO (mud material and engineering), Schlumberger (well and cement logging services), Weatherford (provider of casing accessories), and Tidewater (owner–operator of the offshore supply vessel *Damon B. Bankston*) (Transocean 2011a, 17). Further information is given in Chapter 5.

Six large diesel generators powered the rig's integrated electric plant. Pro-pulsion and dynamic positioning were produced by steerable thruster pods. Gen-erated electrical power was also consumed by hotel loads, drilling equipment loads, and damage control equipment including pumps for firefighting and de-watering. A backup diesel generator, smaller than any of the six main units, pro-vided emergency power for lighting and restarting the main engines in the event of a loss of main power. Propulsion power plays a vital role in maintaining the rig's position, since wind and currents constantly work to move the rig away from the wellhead, risking separation of the riser from the wellhead. Thus, the rig's design and maintenance with regard to sustaining reliable propulsion power play important roles in drilling operations safety, as well as in traditional marine navigation safety.

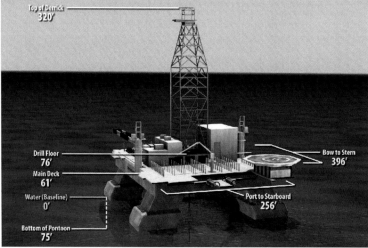

FIGURE 4-1 Basic dimensions of the *Deepwater Horizon* rig while drilling. Source: Chief Counsel 2011, p. 26.

A system of protective electrical and mechanical devices, intended to detect combustible gas and prevent its ignition, was designed into areas of the rig where potentially explosive mixtures of hydrocarbons and air may accumulate if released. Components located in rig zones with the greatest risk of high-gaseous hydrocarbon concentrations were described as "classified," designed to protect against exterior ignition and required to pass tests demonstrating isolation of internal ignition sources from potentially combustible atmospheres. Outside the classified zones, use of standard components without such ignition prevention features was permissible.

Alarms and Indications

The *Deepwater Horizon*'s alarm system was controlled and monitored from the integrated alarm and control system (IACS), which comprised a network of distributed computers. Workstations around the rig displayed the condition of the propulsion system, generators, auxiliaries, and other systems. From the bridge, the watch team could monitor all instrumented activities including dynamic positioning activities, drilling, fire and gas detection, power management, and machinery systems. The integrated system is described in some detail by May and Foss (2000). According to the paper, the dynamic positioning system was a triple-redundant system with dual buses, designed with the intent of being reliable and robust.

As discussed by BP (2010), Republic of the Marshall Islands (2011), and Transocean (2011a), the fire and gas panel monitored fire detectors, combustible gas detectors (CGDs), and toxic gas detectors. There were 27 CGDs on the rig, each of which had an audible and visual alarm. According to BP (2010), the system was designed to have only one CGD at each location. Thirteen of the 27 CGDs had automatic responses, such as securing ventilation fans and all electrical power to an affected area that was in an alarm condition, while the other 14 only had an audible and visual display. The engine room ventilation CGDs did not have an automated response, which required a crew member to validate an alarm in this space before taking manual actions, since securing one or more operating diesel engines could disrupt dynamic positioning of the rig (Transocean 2011a). An emergency disconnect from the well might be necessary if the rig was latched up to the subsea system and dynamic positioning was lost.

Diesel Generator Safety Systems

The diesel engines were fitted with three overspeed shutdown devices that would shut off the fuel, but none of these devices was designed to close off the air intake to the engines directly (USCG 2011). Instead, one of the speed signals was sent to the IACS. If that system determined that the diesel engine was 13 percent above its rated speed, it would cut both the fuel and the air supply to the engine. This was the only overspeed protection on the diesel engines that would automatically cut off the air to the engine. The diesel generator intake air could also have been closed off from the emergency shutdown panels in the driller's shack, the bridge, or the engine control room, or manually at each engine (USCG 2011).

The Disaster

When control of the Macondo well was lost and hydrocarbons were released aboard the *Deepwater Horizon*, the rig suffered two significant explosions before bridge watch standers sounded the general alarm and took steps to attempt actuation of the emergency disconnect system (EDS) (USCG 2011). (See Figure 3-4 for a timeline of the various events leading up to the explosion.) When the gas alarms were triggered, the crew did not take steps to shut down the main engines or stop the flow of outside air into the machinery spaces, which would have isolated potential sources of ignition (USCG 2011). The apparent cause of the explosions was ignition of a combustible mixture of gaseous hydrocarbons (from the well) and air. However, no investigation has determined the precise source of ignition for the explosions.

Loss of power from the two operating diesel generators occurred close to the time of the explosions. Testimony from some of the survivors indicated that the operating diesel generators increased speed in the seconds preceding the explosions and then stopped at the second explosion.[3] Other testimony described a loss of lighting and general electrical power just before the second explosion.[4] It was consistently reported that lighting and other power had failed prior to the diesel generator engines shutting down.[5] No independent data were available to support or refute the witness testimony concerning the sequence of electric plant changes during the disaster. Nonetheless, testimony points to the following as the most likely scenario:

- The hydrocarbon stream resulting from loss of well control flowed from the riser to the top of the derrick.[6]
- Flow was diverted to the mud–gas separator (MGS) system and began to exit at the MGS vents, spewing mud, oil, and gas from the goosenecks to the deck below.[7]

---

[3]Testimony of Randy Ezell, May 28, 2010, Hearing Before the *Deepwater Horizon* Joint Investigation Team, 283-284.

[4]Testimony of James Nicholas Wilson, October 13, 2010, 10; of Stephen Bertone, July 19, 2010, 35; and of Douglas Brown, May 26, 2010, 94-95, Hearing Before the *Deepwater Horizon* Joint Investigation Team.

[5]Testimony of Charles Credeur, May 29, 2010, Hearing Before the *Deepwater Horizon* Joint Investigation Team, 63-64.

[6]Testimony of Micah Sandell, May 29, 2010, Hearing Before the *Deepwater Horizon* Joint Investigation Team, 8, 10, 12.

[7]Testimony of Micah Sandell, May 29, 2010, Hearing Before the *Deepwater Horizon* Joint Investigation Team, 8, 10, 12.

- A cloud of hydrocarbons formed around the rig, in light wind conditions, and quickly expanded to encompass most of the rig (BP 2010, 126–138 and Appendix V, 22-24).
- The running diesel generators ingested a mix of hydrocarbons and air through their induction systems, causing acceleration of the engines and an increase in the generators' speed[8] and thus an increase in the generators' frequencies.
- Engines started to overspeed and power was lost on the rig, as recognized in later analysis of the lost data feed on the real-time data recorder (BP 2010, 111).
- Seconds later, two successive explosions occurred.
- Both operating diesel generator engines shut down.[9]

The only path, other than straight up through the derrick or through the MGS system vents, through which uncontrolled hydrocarbon flow could have been directed is through 14-inch diverter lines, which were positioned to send the flow overboard at about derrick floor level (see Figure 4-2). Testimony cited above indicates that this did not occur, and why there was no hydrocarbon flow along that path remains an unresolved question.[10] According to BP's analysis, the overboard diverter flow of hydrocarbons might have delayed the formation of the explosive cloud that surrounded the rig (BP 2010, 128).

As the rig suffered from a loss of power, explosions, and fire, the bridge team reacted, but confusion clouded the decision process. The general alarm was manually activated by the dynamic positioning officer, and she sent Mayday messages.[11] Senior officers argued about whether the order had been given to initiate an emergency disconnect of the lower marine riser from the blowout preventer (BOP), and they were conflicted about who had the authority to issue that order, the master or the OIM.[12] Before the master and OIM completed discussions about initiating the EDS, the subsea supervisor had already made an attempt to do so, but it was unsuccessful (USCG 2011). The display panels indicated that the disconnect had occurred, but he determined that the MODU was still connected to the riser (USCG 2011).

---

[8]Testimony of Douglas Brown, May 26, 2010, Hearing before the *Deepwater Horizon* Joint Investigation Team, 93-94.

[9]Testimony of Stephen Bertone, July 19, 2010, Hearing before the *Deepwater Horizon* Joint Investigation Team, 35-36.

[10]Testimony of Micah Sandell, May 29, 2010, Hearing Before the *Deepwater Horizon* Joint Investigation Team, 9-11.

[11]Testimony of Andrea Fleytas, October 5, 2010, Hearing Before the *Deepwater Horizon* Joint Investigation Team, 14.

[12]Testimony of Daun Winslow, August 23, 2010, 450-451, and of Stephen Bertone, July 19, 2010, 39, Hearing Before the *Deepwater Horizon* Joint Investigation Team.

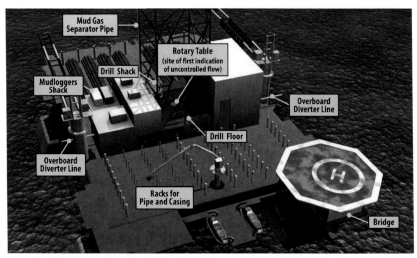

FIGURE 4-2 Illustration of the main deck of the *Deepwater Horizon.* The rig crew could send fluids from the well overboard through the overboard diverter lines. Alternatively, the crew could route flow from the well to an MGS pipe and vent hydrocarbon gas before sending the mud to the mud pits (not shown). Source: Chief Counsel 2011, p. 27.

Assuming that emergency disconnect had occurred, the chief engineer and others attempted unsuccessfully to restart the standby generator in an effort to restore power to pump water for firefighting and power thrusters to reposition the rig.[13] On the basis of the severity of the damage and fire and the inability to restore power, a decision was made to order abandonment of the rig.[14]

All but 11 of the crew survived and were rescued. Most of the survivors followed the abandonment order by making their way to the operable lifeboats. Despite the substantial confusion among rig personnel, evacuation was effected. One hundred personnel left by two lifeboats (combined capacity of 146), seven left in a life raft, and eight jumped into the sea (Transocean 2011a, 201–203). The large number of personnel to escape by lifeboat was attributed to a few key crew members who delayed launching until they had boarded as many as possible.[15,16]

---

[13]Testimony of Stephen Bertone, July 19, 2010, Hearing Before the *Deepwater Horizon* Joint Investigation Team, 39-40.

[14]Testimony of Stephen Bertone, July 19, 2010, Hearing Before the *Deepwater Horizon* Joint Investigation Team, 39-40.

[15]Testimony of Micah Sandell, May 29, 2010, Hearing Before the *Deepwater Horizon* Joint Investigation Team, 11-13.

[16]Testimony of Daun Winslow, August 23, 2010, Hearing Before the *Deepwater Horizon* Joint Investigation Team, 452.

In the confusion of the evacuation, no complete muster (headcount) of personnel was conducted onboard the *Deepwater Horizon* (USCG 2011). At least two of the four senior merchant marine officers expected to be most knowledgeable about coordinating a mass evacuation of the rig were not available to participate in the muster or in the launching of either lifeboat, because they were carrying out other duties. Also, when fire and abandonment drills were conducted, the marine crew and the drill crew did not collectively participate because of drilling operations (USCG 2011).[17]

The supply vessel, *Damon B. Bankston,* was alongside the rig when the blowout occurred. The vessel's "fast rescue craft" was instrumental in the rescue of survivors who had jumped into the sea. The ship's crew also helped in freeing the life raft from a rope that tethered the raft to the rig and in towing the raft to safety (USCG 2011, xiv). The rig crew had not practiced a life raft launch, and the raft occupants were unable to release the connecting line on their own (USCG 2011, xv, 64).

After all survivors had been accounted for, it was determined that the 11 killed were crew last seen on the drill floor, the mud pump room, and the shaker house. All of those areas were broadly exposed to the gaseous hydrocarbon flow erupting from the well through the MGS system vents.[18] No protection system was built into these working areas of the rig to deflect the effects of explosion from those who were exposed.

Complex Operations in Hazardous Environments

Conduct of marine exploration drilling from the *Deepwater Horizon* and other deepwater rigs is an extremely complex engineering operation in an unforgiving maritime environment. Management of those complexities by the responsible companies during the drilling and temporary abandonment of the Macondo well was unsuccessful in preventing loss of life, injury, and extensive pollution of the environment. This disaster underscores the need for instilling an effective systems safety approach for offshore drilling operations (see Chapter 5). Programs for system safety that were established for other safety-critical large-scale activities can be a source of useful guidance.

In the aftermath of the loss of a space shuttle, the Columbia Accident Investigation Board (CAIB) in 2003 examined the U.S. Navy's Submarine Safety Program (SUBSAFE)[19] as one example of successful implementation of system

---

[17]In its response to the U.S. Coast Guard report (USCG 2011), Transocean (2011b) noted that "To require on-duty drill crews to participate in fire drills would be imprudent and unsafe—during the fire drill no one would be left to monitor the well."

[18]In its report, the U.S. Coast Guard (USCG 2011, x) concludes that the crew on the drill floor and in the mud pits were likely killed during the initial explosions.

[19]SUBSAFE was implemented in 1963, after the loss of the USS *Thresher.* Since SUBSAFE was implemented nearly 50 years ago, no SUBSAFE-certified submarine has been lost at sea. This is far different from the situation that existed before SUBSAFE,

safety (CAIB 2003, 182–184). Among the observations made by CAIB with regard to the Navy's submarine programs, the following highlights provide useful guidance in considering the oil and gas industry's and government's necessary responses to the *Deepwater Horizon* disaster:

- Technical requirements are clearly documented and achievable, with minimal "tailoring" or granting of waivers.
- A separate compliance verification organization independently assesses program management.
- There is a strong safety culture that emphasizes understanding and learning from past failures.
- Extensive safety training is based on past accidents.
- The safety program structure is enhanced by the clarity, uniformity, and consistency of submarine safety requirements and responsibilities. Program managers are not permitted to "tailor" requirements without approval from the organization with final authority for technical requirements and the organization that verifies compliance with critical design and process requirements.
- Compliance with critical design and process requirements is independently verified by a highly capable centralized organization that also "owns" (i.e., accepts responsibility for) the processes and monitors the program.

FINDINGS

On the basis of the preceding discussion and the information obtained from witness testimony at investigative hearings, presentations to the committee, and previously published reports, the committee has developed the following findings, as well as the observations and recommendations provided in subsequent sections.

Explosions and Fire on the *Deepwater Horizon*

Summary Finding 4.1: **Once well control was lost, the large quantities of gaseous hydrocarbons released onto the *Deepwater Horizon*, exacerbated by low wind velocity and questionable venting selection, made ignition all but inevitable.**

Finding 4.1a: **Uncontrolled flow of hydrocarbons through the derrick resulted in a huge cloud of combustible atmosphere surrounding the rig.**

---

when, on average, a submarine was lost every 3 years to noncombat causes from 1915 to 1963. Additional discussion of the safety system aspect of SUBSAFE is provided by Presidential Commission (2011).

Finding 4.1b: The rig was not designed to prevent explosion or fire once it was surrounded by the extent of combustible atmosphere facing the *Deepwater Horizon.*

Finding 4.1c: Hydrocarbon flow was not redirected overboard. Overboard discharge of the blowout might have delayed the explosion and fire aboard the rig.

Finding 4.1d: Explosions and subsequent fire are suspected to have resulted from ignition of the surrounding combustible cloud; the source of the ignition cannot be definitively determined.

The Rig's Power Supply

Finding 4.2: Loss of power led to a broad range of effects including loss of firefighting ability, position-keeping ability, and overall situational control.

Finding 4.2a: The rig's dynamic positioning system operated as designed until the loss of power disabled the rig's ability to maintain station or reposition under control.

Finding 4.2b: Backup system designs did not ensure reliable power.

Finding 4.2c: The standby generator did not automatically start and could not be started in manual mode, indicating deficient reliability in the backup system needed to restore main generator power.

Finding 4.2d: Poor performance by the standby diesel generator may indicate that insufficient environmental testing was specified for this critical, last-resort power system to demonstrate robust capability or any local indication of generator starting availability.

Alarm and Indication Systems, Procedures, and Training

Finding 4.3: Alarm and indication systems, procedures, and training were insufficient to ensure timely and effective actions to prevent the explosions or respond to save the rig.

Finding 4.3a: The rig design did not employ automatic methods to react to indications of a massive blowout, leaving reactions entirely in the hands of the surviving crew.

Finding 4.3b: The crew was ill-prepared for the scale of this disaster.

Finding 4.3c: Watch officers were not trained to respond to the conditions faced in this incident.

Finding 4.3d: Emergency procedures did not equip the watch standers with immediate actions to minimize damage and loss of life.

Finding 4.3e: The training routine did not include any full rig drills designed to develop and maintain crew proficiency in reacting to major incidents.

Finding 4.3f: Training of key personnel did not include realistic blowout scenarios or the handling of multiple concurrent failures.

Finding 4.3g: Crew members lacked cross-rate training to understand rig total systems and components. As a result, many of the crew were inadequately prepared to react to the incident.

Decision Authority and Command

Finding 4.4: Confusion existed about decision authority and command. Uncertainty as to whether the rig was under way or moored to the wellhead contributed to the confusion on the bridge and may have impaired timely disconnect.

Life-Saving Equipment

Finding 4.5: The U.S. Coast Guard's requirement for the number and placement of lifeboats was shown to be prudent and resulted in sufficient lifeboat capacity for effective rig abandonment. The Coast Guard's investigation report (USCG 2011) notes a lack of heat shielding to protect escape paths and life-saving equipment.

Lack of Fail-Safe Design and Testing, Training, and Operating Practices Aboard the Rig

Finding 4.6: The above findings indicate that the lack of fail-safe design and testing, training, and operating practices aboard the rig contributed to loss of the rig and loss of life. The chain of events that began downhole (see Chapter 2) could have been interrupted at many points, such as at the wellhead by the BOP (see Chapter 3) or aboard the rig, where the flow might have been directed overboard or where the rig itself might have been disconnected from the well and repositioned. Had the rig been able to disconnect, the primary fuel load for the fire would have been eliminated.

OBSERVATIONS

Evacuation

Observation 4.1: The actions of some crew members in requiring due consideration of additional survivors before launching lifeboats, despite the fearsome fires engulfing the rig, are commendable and were important in the highly successful evacuation.

Observation 4.2: The attempts to start the standby diesel generator and restore power for damage control were acts of bravery.

Observation 4.3: Conditions of explosion, fire, loss of lighting, toxic gas, and eventual flooding and sinking could have resulted in many more injuries or deaths if not for the execution of the rig's evacuation.

Rules for Rig Propulsion Control Systems

Observation 4.4: American Bureau of Shipping (ABS)[20] rules require that propulsion control systems for MODUs shall "in general" comply with the Steel Vessel Rules. This requirement may give rise to ambiguity concerning primary control and monitoring systems on MODUs.

RECOMMENDATIONS

Summary Recommendation 4.1: Instrumentation and expert system decision aids should be used to provide timely warning of loss of well control to drillers on the rig (and ideally to onshore drilling monitors as well). If the warning is inhibited or not addressed in an appropriate time interval, autonomous operation of the blind shear rams, EDS, general alarm, and other safety systems on the rig should occur.[21]

---

[20]As a classification society, the role of ABS is to verify that marine vessels and offshore structures comply with rules that the society has established for design, construction, and periodic survey (ABS 2011).

[21]Although it was presented in Chapter 3, the recommendation is also presented here to underscore that the rig, riser, BOP, and drilling equipment are an integrated system.

Safety System Design

Recommendation 4.2: Rigs should be designed so that their instrumentation, expert system decision aids, and safety systems are robust and highly reliable under all foreseeable normal and extreme operating conditions. The design should account for hazards that may result from drilling operations and attachment to an uncontrolled well. The aggregate effects of cascading casualties and failures should be considered to avoid the coupling of failure modes to the maximum reasonable extent.

Recommendation 4.3: Industry and regulators should develop fail-safe design requirements for the combined systems of rig, riser, BOP, drilling equipment, and well to ensure that (*a*) blowouts are prevented and (*b*) if a blowout should occur the hydrocarbon flow will be quickly isolated and the rig can disconnect and reposition. The criteria for these requirements should be maximum reasonable assurance of (*a*) and (*b*) and successful crew evacuation under both scenarios.

Recommendation 4.4: Industry and regulators should implement a method of design review for systemic risks for future well design that uses a framework with attributes similar to those of the Department of Defense *Standard Practice for System Safety* (DoD 2000), which articulates standard practices for system safety for the U.S. military, to address the complex and integrated "system of systems" challenges faced in safely operating deepwater drilling rigs. The method should take into consideration the coupled effects of well design and rig design. (See Chapter 5 for a discussion of safety system qualities.)

Recommendation 4.5: Industry should institute design improvements in systems, technology, training, and qualification to ensure that crew members are best prepared to cope with serious casualties.

Recommendation 4.6: ABS should eliminate any ambiguity in its rules requiring that propulsion control systems for MODUs shall "in general" comply with the Steel Vessel Rules. All of the primary control and monitoring systems and critical backup systems on these MODUs should be designed and tested to the highest standards in the industry.

Automatic Redirection of Hydrocarbon Flow Overboard

Recommendation 4.7: Industry should develop and implement passive or automatic methods to redirect hydrocarbon flow overboard. Ideally, the methods would include some artificial intelligence capability to evaluate the magnitude of the flow and prevailing wind.

Recovery of Main Electrical Power

Recommendation 4.8: Recovery of main electrical power is a vital capability for MODUs. Industry should ensure that standby generator systems will be reliable and robust for automatic starting. Moreover, standby generator location, controls, and power lines should be positioned to minimize the likelihood of damage from fire or explosions in the main engine room or from other casualties affecting the primary electric power system.

Capturing and Preserving Data for Future Investigations

Recommendation 4.9: Data logger systems should be designed for handling the bandwidth of sensor data that may arise under the most stressing casualty conditions. The systems should be able to transmit in real time to shore so that accurate records are potentially available for determination of root cause in subsequent investigation.

Alarms and Indicators

Recommendation 4.10: Inhibition of alarms should be allowed only when approved by a senior officer in the vessel. Regulators should require that the master, OIM, and chief engineer review periodically the status of alarms and indications and take action to resolve conditions of complacent behavior. This should be a standard item of regulatory and class inspections.

Recommendation 4.11: Drilling rig contractors should review designs to ensure adequate redundancy in alarms and indicators in key areas of the rig.

Education and Training of Rig Personnel

Recommendation 4.12: Drilling rig contractors should require realistic and effective training in operations and emergency situations for key personnel before assignment to any rig. Industry should also require that personnel aboard the rig achieve and maintain a high degree of expertise in their assigned watch station, including formal qualification and periodic reexamination.

Recommendation 4.13: **Realistic simulators should be used to expose key operators to conditions of stress that are expected in major conflagrations, including heat and loss of visibility (see Chapter 5).**

Recommendation 4.14: **Realistic major drill scenarios with independent oversight should be part of the normal routine at sea.**

Recommendation 4.15: **Regulators should require that all permanent crew on a rig achieve a basic level of qualification in damage control and escape systems to ensure that all hands are able to contribute to resolving a major casualty.**

Recommendation 4.16: **Regulators should increase the qualification requirements of the OIM to reflect a level of experience commensurate with the consequences of potential failure in his or her decision making.**

A comparison of the current minimum qualification requirements of an OIM with those of a rig master shows that the OIM requirements are much less rigorous today than is indicated by the OIM's significant responsibilities for well control (46 CFR 11.404 and 46 CFR 11.470). For example, a typical master of unrestricted tonnage has a 4-year degree in a recognized maritime academy deck officer curriculum or more than 3 years of relevant rating sea time, plus additional years of sea experience in successive promotion roles from third mate through second mate and chief mate. In contrast, one may be licensed as an OIM with as little as 4 years (or 2 years plus an engineering technology degree) of experience aboard MODUs in roles as assistant driller, assistant tool pusher, electrician, or crane operator; 14 days of experience as a supervisor of those ratings; and a 5-day course in stability for OIMs.

Definition of Command at Sea

Recommendation 4.17: **Definition of command at sea should be absolutely unambiguous and should not change during emergencies.**

Recommendation 4.18: **Regulators should establish the unity of command and clearly articulate the hierarchy of roles and responsibilities of company man, master, and OIM.**

Appointment of Certification Authority

Recommendation 4.19: **Operating companies and drilling contractors should institute a certification authority, accountable to the head of** the company, to act as the senior corporate official responsible and accountable for meeting the conditions set out in a safety management system (see Chapter 5). This appointment should provide a powerful voice for safe execution of operations and surety in dealing with emergencies: the official should have the authority and responsibility to stop work if necessary.

System Safety Certification

Recommendation 4.20: Industry and regulators should consider relevant aspects of programs for system safety certification that were established for other safety-critical large-scale activities, such as the U.S. Navy's Submarine Safety Program, as guidance in developing a response to the *Deepwater Horizon* incident.

Recommendation 4.21: Industry and regulators should develop and implement a certification to ensure that design requirements, material condition, maintenance, modernization, operating and emergency instructions, manning, and training are all effective in meeting the requirements of Recommendation 4.3 throughout the rig's service life.

Recommendation 4.22: Regulators should require that the rig, the entire system, and the crew be examined annually by an experienced and objective outside team to achieve and maintain certification in operational drilling safeguards. The consequence of unsatisfactory findings should be suspension of the crew's operation except under special supervisory conditions.

5

Industry Management of Offshore Drilling

This chapter assesses the extent to which the actions, policies, and procedures of corporations involved in the Macondo well–*Deepwater Horizon* incident failed to provide an effective system safety approach commensurate with the risks of drilling the well. The chapter also assesses the education, training, and certification of key personnel and the extent of industrywide learning from past incidents. Finally, the chapter provides recommendations for improving various aspects of industry management.

Offshore drilling in the United States is currently carried out through an aggregation of drilling contractors, service companies, and consultants brought together by an operating company, which is the company designated to conduct the operations of the well. Deepwater operations are some of the most complex and most risky ventures conducted by commercial enterprises. This is particularly true in regions, such as the Gulf of Mexico, where wells are drilled in water depths of up to 10,000 feet, drilling depths can exceed 20,000 feet, and geologic formation pressures can exceed 20,000 pounds per square inch. Many of the formations are prolific and can produce thousands of barrels of oil and millions of cubic feet of gas per day. As with other complex industrial systems, the safe and efficient functioning of offshore drilling operations depends on the culture of the organizations involved, which includes interactions among human, organizational, and technological subsystems (Meshkati 1995).

Each organization and person involved in offshore drilling operations is expected to maintain a strong focus on safety. Many operating companies adhere to a rigorous safety checklist and in many cases perform safety audits of their contractors, service companies, and others. However, over the course of time, offshore accidents occur that are attributable to the lack of one or several elements of an integrated safety management system or to a lack of diligence in executing those elements that are part of the contractor's systems.

The aspect of safety management addressing hazards that lead to accidents on the scale of one or a few workers, such as slipping and falling or injuries that occur during a crane-lifting activity, is commonly termed *occupational safety* (also referred to as personal safety or worker safety). In contrast, other offshore drilling hazards can lead to accidents on a much larger scale, potentially involving multiple fatalities, substantial property loss, and extensive environmental damage. Hazards that can cause catastrophic effects are within the realm of *system safety*.[1] This term refers to an engineering and management approach used to ensure that safety is built into a system with the objective of preventing or significantly reducing the likelihood of a potential accident. [See Rasmussen (1997), Rasmussen and Svedung (2000), and Leveson (2011) for additional discussion of system safety.]

The *Ocean Ranger* mobile offshore drilling unit (MODU) incident in 1982 involved a failed ballast control system and a ballast control operator who was not properly trained to respond to this particular event (Hickman 1984). The MODU sank and all personnel were lost—most, if not all, because of the harsh cold conditions. Industry's response to the *Ocean Ranger* disaster resulted in a major shift in ballast control training and the introduction of simulators to train ballast control operators. The disaster also led the offshore industry to improve the training of rig personnel in survival skills and the procedures for abandonment of a drilling vessel. Those efforts encouraged the worldwide development of survival schools. Industry's response to the event also demonstrated the need for a preemptive overall safety strategy. Even though the *Ocean Ranger* disaster was not a well blowout event, it demonstrated the importance of understanding the ramifications of the total system safety of an offshore operation.

Another example is provided by the *Piper Alpha* platform disaster, which occurred in the North Sea in 1988. A gas leak resulting from a faulty maintenance operation ignited and exploded on the platform, causing a large-scale fire and a disaster that resulted in 167 deaths. The incident showed what damage could occur essentially from an accumulation of management errors (Cullen 1990; Paté-Cornell 1993); it became a turning point in the way industry addressed the safety of its offshore operations. Furthermore, the U.K. government changed the way it regulated the offshore oil and gas industry by moving to a performance-based form of regulation, sometimes referred to as a safety case approach (see Chapter 6).

Although a company's fundamental approach to safety can affect both occupational and system safety, an effective occupational safety program will not necessarily be indicative of an effective approach for managing system safety. Larger-scale accidents can arise from many different causes that are mostly unrelated to the factors targeted by occupational safety programs. However, an effective system safety program can result in reduced injuries and save lives (CCPS 1992). Therefore, both types of safety are of value to workers. Given the

---

[1]In some industries (e.g., chemical) the term is also referred to as *process safety*.

charge to the committee, this chapter and the following one focus on system safety.

SAFETY CULTURE

The steps taken by the nuclear power and other safety-critical industries to improve system safety are reminiscent of the challenges presently confronting the offshore drilling industry. Although there are significant differences between the oil and gas industry and other industries (as discussed in this chapter), the safety framework and perspectives developed by those other industries can provide useful insights. According to the Swedish Radiation Safety Authority, an organization has good potential for safety when it has developed a *safety culture* that shows a willingness and an ability to understand risks and manage activities so that safety is taken into account (Oedewald et al. 2011). Other industries, regulatory agencies, trade associations, and professional associations have also addressed safety culture (for example, see Reason 1997; U.S. NRC 2009, 2011; NEI 2009; CCPS 2005; IAEA 1992).

The U.K. Health and Safety Executive defines safety culture as "the product of individual group values, attitudes and perceptions, competencies and patterns of behavior that determine the commitment to, and the style and proficiency of, an organization's health and safety management." Creating safety culture means instilling attitudes and procedures in individuals and organizations ensuring that safety issues are treated as high priority, too. A facility fostering strong safety culture would encourage employees to cultivate a questioning attitude and a rigorous and prudent approach to all aspects of their jobs and to set up necessary open communication between line workers and middle and upper management (Meshkati 1999).

An effective safety culture embodies the following generic traits:[2]

- *Leadership safety values and actions:* Safety is treated as a complex and systemic phenomenon. It is also a genuine value that is reflected in the decision making and daily activities of an organization in managing risks and preventing accidents.

- *Personal accountability:* All individuals take personal responsibility for safety and contribute to overall safety.

- *Problem identification and resolution:* Issues potentially affecting safety are readily identified, fully evaluated, and promptly addressed and corrected.

- *Work processes:* The process of planning and controlling work activities is implemented so that system safety is maintained. The most serious safety issues get the greatest attention.

---

[2]The traits are adapted from the U.S. Nuclear Regulatory Commission Safety Culture Policy Statement (U.S. NRC 2011).

- *Continuous learning:* Opportunities to learn about ways to ensure safety are sought out and implemented by organizations and personnel. Hazards, procedures, and job responsibilities are thoroughly understood. Safety culture strives to be flexible and adjustable so that personnel are able to identify and react appropriately to various indications of hazard.

- *Environment for raising concerns:* A safety-conscious work environment is maintained, where personnel feel free to raise safety concerns without fear of retaliation, intimidation, harassment, or discrimination. They perceive their reporting as being meaningful to their organizations and thus avoid underreporting.

- *Effective safety communication:* Communications maintain a focus on safety. Knowledge and experience are shared across organizational boundaries, especially when different companies are involved in various phases of the same project. Knowledge and experience are also shared vertically within an organization.

- *Respectful work environment:* Trust and respect permeate the organization.

- *Questioning attitude:* Individuals avoid complacency and continuously challenge existing conditions and activities to identify discrepancies that might result in unsafe conditions. A subordinate does not hesitate to question a supervisor, and a contractor employee does not hesitate to question an employee of an operating company.

Investigations of several large-scale accidents in recent years provide clear illustrations of the consequences of a deficient safety culture. A collision of two trains of the Washington Metropolitan Area Transit Authority (WMATA) Metrorail that occurred in June 2009 resulted in nine deaths and multiple passenger injuries. The National Transportation Safety Board found that WMATA failed to implement many significant attributes of a sound safety program (NTSB 2010). As another example, explosions and fires at the BP Texas City Refinery in March 2005 killed 15 people and injured 180 others. The U.S. Chemical Safety and Hazard Investigation Board concluded that the disaster was caused by organizational and safety deficiencies at all levels of the BP Corporation (CSB 2007). These accidents underscore the importance of organizations being proactive and appropriately focused on system safety.

High-Reliability Organizations

Technically complex organizations that are designed and managed to operate safely in environments where a system failure can result in a catastrophic accident are referred to as high-reliability organizations (HROs) (Roberts and Rousseau 1989; Weick and Sutcliffe 2001; Carnes 2011). HROs repeatedly accomplish their missions while avoiding catastrophic events despite significant hazards, dynamic tasks, time constraints, and complex technologies (Hartley et al. 2008). Personnel training is usually provided in a team setting and is facilitated through simulators to provide realism and improve the team's work process and ability to handle unexpected occurrences.

HROs are involved in the design, testing, operation, and maintenance of nuclear power plants, air traffic control systems, military submarines, and other systems. In a study of the U.S. Navy nuclear submarine fleet, Bierly and Spender (1995) concluded that "the nuclear submarine illustrates how culture, as a higher level system of knowledge and experience, can interact with and support a bureaucracy to transform a high risk system into a high reliability system."

Conflicting Objectives

HROs often rely on risk assessment to inform their decision-making and planning processes for carrying out operations. The two key elements of risk in this context are the likelihood of a catastrophic system failure occurring and the consequences of such an occurrence. According to Bea et al. (2009), proper problem definition for risk analysis of complex systems considers all the variables of a system including psychological, social, organizational, and political processes as well as technological and engineering practices. Probabilistic risk assessment can be used to assess safety within a complex technologic organization by relating failure probability to performance within various aspects of the organization (Paté-Cornell 1990).

When business considerations (e.g., cost and schedule) come in conflict with minimizing risk, a disciplined approach is needed to weigh process effectiveness against the level of risk for an upcoming action or series of actions. A sound safety culture ensures that the organization can address conflicting objectives without compromising system safety and can keep the likelihood of a system failure as low as practicable (see Chapter 6). In its publication *HSE and Culture* (PSA 2004), the Petroleum Safety Authority of Norway provides petroleum exploration and production companies with a set of useful questions that guide a company in dealing with conflicting objectives:

- Are conflicting objectives discussed in a specific and constructive manner?
- Have clear, realistic, and accepted criteria been established for the way operational personnel should deal with normal conflicts between objectives?
- Are procedures and job descriptions adjusted to ensure a balance between safety and efficient performance of the work?
- Who decides the procedures? Do operational personnel participate in maintaining procedures and job descriptions?
- Is HSE monitored on a par with production, quality, and economics?

System Safety in Offshore Drilling Operations

Over the past 20 years, an offshore industry has evolved to meet the technical challenge of discovering and producing oil and gas under hostile conditions. Land-based drilling operations have been standardized to a great extent over the past 50 years because well control equipment placed on site is accessible and there is substantial capacity for rapid escape from an out-of-control well. However, the complexity and unique nature of offshore drilling did not develop similarly robust standardized operations commensurate with the risks involved. Offshore drilling in deeper water incorporates the complexity of controlling subsea blowout preventer (BOP) systems that must withstand the hostile environment of water depths of up to 10,000 feet, as well as control systems, seals, connectors, and valves that all must function flawlessly, with minimal need for preventive maintenance, for the BOP to work properly. In addition, a riser system that is used to connect the rig's circulation system to the well and carry the choke and kill lines necessary for well operation must perform reliably.

Sophisticated firmware[3] and software provide much of the control functionality. To maintain their position over the well, MODUs increasingly rely on dynamic positioning by using multiple thrusters that are computer controlled. In the event of thruster failures or power outages and blackout, each rig has an automated disconnect system that, on manual initiation by rig personnel, is designed to release the MODU from the well. The sequence of actions to activate the subsea BOP system, shear the drill pipe, shut in the well, and release the riser from the BOP involves commands and functionality that are highly automated and complex (see Chapter 3). However, the BOP and its components are rarely, if ever, field-tested as a full system because of logistical difficulties, concerns about degradation of future performance capabilities, the expense associated with conducting such a system test, and lack of a regulatory requirement. Instead, tests of individual components of the BOP technology, riser, and riser disconnect are assumed to constitute effective tests of the entire system.

In addition, the drilling equipment is highly automated, with a sophisticated system for mud circulation, heave compensation, top drives, automated pipe-handling equipment, and sensors positioned on most of the equipment to detect rig activities and sense hydrocarbons.

Well operations typically include personnel from multiple contractors involved in monitoring and operating the complex system. There are drilling contractor personnel (some of whom may be subcontractors or consultants) and support service personnel for running casing, cementing, maintaining the drilling fluids, and monitoring the downhole progress of the drilling operation. In addition, there are specialty contractors for logging, running wellheads, directing remotely operated vehicles, and conducting a plethora of other services and activities. The drilling contractor—focused on running the MODU, the subsea operation, and drilling equipment—relies on the operating company to provide

---

[3]Firmware is fixed software used to control electronic devices.

the basic well plan, which includes formations to be drilled, mud weights needed, and casing string and cementing designs. The operator relies on suppliers, and in many cases consultants, to design the casing strings and on other companies to design the cementing composition and the procedures for cementing the casing. In general, the running of the MODU and the downhole activities is complex, and certain activities are often implemented separately from the others. Furthermore, the committee has observed from presentations made by industry representatives[4] that the level of safety training, experience, and knowledge of the overall operation for drilling the well tends to be uneven for personnel of operating companies and their contractors. However, as the entity that created and oversees the plan for the well, the operating company holds the overall decision-making responsibility.

A fundamental aspect that should be common to all companies is effective system safety that embodies the safety culture traits discussed earlier in this chapter. Despite the complexity of deepwater offshore drilling, the committee has observed from presentations made by industry representatives (as mentioned above) that the parties involved tend not to exhibit an overall systems approach for addressing the multiple interacting safety issues involved in the subsea, MODU, and drilling activities. One indication of the lack of appreciation for an overall system safety view is the limited level of system safety training provided by the operators and contractors. Although differences among various types of industries and other organizations do not allow for exact comparisons, the extent of system safety training provided by the oil and gas industry appears to be modest compared with that provided by the military, nuclear power, and aerospace industries, which also face complex challenges and hazardous conditions.

The offshore industry evolved over the past 20 years. During that period, significant industry change occurred. Some exploration and production (E&P) companies merged and consolidated (see Figure 5-1), sometimes divesting their research and development (R&D) capacity and delegating many of the responsibilities and shedding expertise they once held. Some E&P companies that previously had in-house capacities to design a complete well plan and supervise the various operations became more reliant on third-party service companies and consultants to take over those key roles. Some companies have in-house cementing expertise and many do not. Some companies train and develop their supervising personnel, and some companies hire consultants to provide this service. Although relying on outside expertise to deal with the increasing complexity of offshore drilling may be more cost-effective, doing so tends to reduce the level of consistency across the industry with regard to who does the well planning,

---

[4]Members heard presentations from industry representatives during various committee meetings held over the course of this study. In addition, committee members heard presentations from industry representatives at meetings of the Marine Board of Investigation, the National Commission on the BP Deepwater Horizon Oil Spill and Offshore Drilling, and the U.S. Chemical Safety Board.

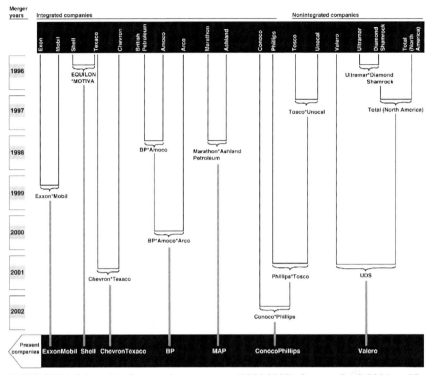

FIGURE 5-1 Selected major petroleum mergers (1996-2002). Source: GAO 2004, p. 37.

what a well plan should be, what type of experience is required for complex deepwater operations, and who monitors and is responsible for the overall integrity of the well.

In essence, the offshore industry is fragmented into a large number of service providers and independent agents with specific roles for drilling offshore wells. This arrangement tends not to allow for recognition of the system-level challenges of handling a multitude of service providers, often with different goals, safety practices, experience levels, and training. This functional diversity among team members may lead to differences in interpretations of what is needed for a team to be successful (Cronin and Weingart 2007). Also, regulators in the United States did not keep up with the technological advances made by the operating companies in dealing with the complexity of deepwater operations (see Chapter 6). Hence, the checks and balances supposedly provided by the regulators did not evolve in proportion to the complexity of offshore operations.

The multiple companies involved in drilling the Macondo well exhibited the complex structure of the offshore oil and gas industry and the division of technical expertise among the contractors engaged in the drilling effort. BP, an E&P company, leased Mississippi Canyon Block 252 in 2008 for oil and gas exploration.[5] BP later sold interests in the lease to Anadarko Petroleum, an independent exploration company (25 percent share) and MOEX, a subsidiary of Mitsui Oil Exploration (10 percent share). BP was the majority owner of the lease (65 percent share). As the operator, BP designed the well and specified how it was to be drilled, cased, completed, and temporarily abandoned. BP employed various contractors to perform the work of drilling and constructing the well. BP's well site leaders were the personnel on the *Deepwater Horizon* rig who supervised operations and coordinated the activities of contractors.

Transocean, a contractor of offshore drilling rigs, was hired by BP to perform services for the *Deepwater Horizon* rig. As part of this arrangement, Transocean provided personnel for drilling, marine operations, and maintenance. Transocean supervisory personnel included the offshore installation manager (OIM), who coordinated rig operations with BP's well site leaders and managed the Transocean crew; the master, who was responsible for all marine operations when the rig traveled from one location to another; and a senior tool pusher, who supervised the tool pushers, who in turn coordinated drilling operations carried out by the drillers and assistant drillers.

Other contractors and manufacturers involved in the Macondo well included the following:

- *Cameron,* a manufacturer of well drilling equipment and well construction components, manufactured the *Deepwater Horizon*'s BOP.
- *Dril-Quip,* a manufacturer of components used in the construction of oil wells, manufactured the wellhead assembly used at the Macondo well, including the casing hanger, seal assembly, and lockdown sleeve components.
- *Halliburton* is an oil field service provider. BP contracted with Halliburton to provide cementing services and related expertise. Halliburton designed and pumped the cement for the casing strings in the well.
- *M-I SWACO* is a subsidiary of Schlumberger. BP contracted with M-I SWACO to provide specialized drilling mud and mud engineering services on the *Deepwater Horizon*; its personnel operated the rig's mud system.
- *Schlumberger* is a provider of a variety of oil field services. BP contracted with Schlumberger to deliver specialized well and cement logging services on the *Deepwater Horizon*. Schlumberger provided well logging services used in the evaluation of the well.
- *Sperry Sun* is a subsidiary of Halliburton. BP contracted with Sperry Sun to install a well monitoring system on the *Deepwater Horizon*. Sperry provided mud loggers to monitor and interpret the data it generated.
- *Weatherford* is a manufacturer of well construction components. BP contracted with Weatherford to provide casing accessories, including centralizers, the float collar, and the shoe track on the *Deepwater Horizon*. Weatherford

---

[5]See Chief Counsel (2011) for additional information on the roles of companies involved in drilling the Macondo well.

also provided personnel to advise on the installation and operation of its equipment.

As discussed in Chapters 2, 3, and 4, the Macondo well–*Deepwater Horizon* event was precipitated by multiple flawed decisions, leading to an uncontrolled blowout that caused loss of life, injuries, and severe negative public and environmental impacts. Involved in those decisions were the operator, drilling contractor, and service companies.[6] The complex interaction of the corporations and government agencies was not managed at a systemic level to anticipate the possible safety shortfalls that ultimately led to the well blowout. This was evidenced by a substantial number of decisions and actions that are inconsistent with the characteristics of a robust safety culture and HRO discussed earlier in the chapter:

- While the geologic conditions encountered in the Macondo well posed challenges to the drilling team, alternative completion techniques and operational processes were available that could have been utilized to prepare the well for temporary abandonment safely (see Chapter 2).
- The design and execution of a cementing program were flawed (see Chapter 2).
- The execution and interpretation of the negative pressure test of the well were flawed. The test was deemed a success even though the pressure buildup actually meant that the test had failed (see Chapter 2).
- No cement bond log was run to investigate the condition of the cement. The well design placed the float collar above the bottom of the deepest reservoir and would have prevented the log from investigating the lower sections of the well in which cement had been pumped (see Chapter 2).
- Evidence available prior to the blowout indicated that the flapper valves in the float collar probably failed to seal, but this evidence was not acted on at the time (see Chapter 2).
- The approach chosen for well completion failed to provide adequate margins of safety and led to multiple potential failure mechanisms. Drilling mud was replaced with seawater, and the annular preventer in the BOP was opened on the assumption that the well was under control (see Chapter 2).
- The crew did not recognize the signs of the impending blowout in time to take the appropriate action. Several signs were missed that should have indicated to the crew that hydrocarbons from the reservoir were flowing into the well (see Chapter 3).

---

[6]As mentioned in the preface, this report does not attempt to assign responsibility for the incident to specific individuals or corporations, nor does it attempt to make a systematic assessment of the extent to which the parties involved complied with applicable regulations.

- The BOP system was neither designed nor tested for the dynamic conditions that most likely existed at the time that attempts were made to recapture well control. Furthermore, the design, test, operation, and maintenance of the BOP system were not consistent with a high-reliability, fail-safe device (see Chapter 3).

- The decision was made to defer maintenance on the annular preventers of the BOP following the March 8th "well control event" (see Chapter 3).

- The rig crew was ill prepared for the scale of this disaster. Alarm and indication systems, procedures, and training were insufficient to ensure timely and effective actions to prevent the explosions or respond to save the rig (see Chapter 4).

- Confusion existed about decision authority and command. Uncertainty as to whether the rig was under way or moored to the wellhead contributed to the confusion on the bridge and may have impaired timely disconnect (see Chapter 4).

- Once the fire started on the rig, it took more than 7 minutes until an attempt was made to activate the emergency disconnect system, which should have closed the blind shear ram and disconnected the lower marine riser package (see Chapter 3).

Previous reports have evaluated the performance of the companies involved in the Macondo well–*Deepwater Horizon* incident (BOEMRE 2011; Chief Counsel 2011; DHSG 2011; Presidential Commission 2011; USCG 2011). The reports have found that technical failures, such as those discussed in this report, can be traced back to management processes that did not provide adequate controls over the uncertainties of human decision making, particularly given the potential consequences as evidenced by the Macondo blowout. Management processes failed to adequately identify and mitigate risks created by operational decisions before the blowout, communicate critical information, train key engineering and rig personnel, and ensure that measures taken to save time and reduce costs did not adversely affect overall risk. A substantial compilation and discussion of witness testimony, written communications, and other information concerning management performance are presented in those reports. While the available evidence does not indicate a specific circumstance in which an explicit decision was made to accept risk to save costs, the committee notes that such trades are an inherent part of drilling operations and that processes to evaluate such trades properly are essential.

The committee's findings presented in this report and the findings of other related reports indicate that industrial management involved with drilling the Macondo well had not adequately understood and coped with the system safety challenges presented by offshore drilling operations. This raises questions concerning industry's overall safety preparedness, the ability to handle the complexities of deepwater operations, industry oversight to approve and monitor well plans and operational practices, and personnel competency and training.

Questions have also been raised as to whether a process is in place to give adequate consideration to the overall risks associated with drilling a Macondo-type well in the Gulf of Mexico.

Summary Finding 5.1: **The actions, policies, and procedures of the corporations involved did not provide an effective system safety approach commensurate with the risks of the Macondo well. The lack of a strong safety culture resulting from a deficient overall systems approach to safety is evident in the multiple flawed decisions that led to the blowout. Industrial management involved with the Macondo well–** *Deepwater Horizon* **disaster failed to appreciate or plan for the safety challenges presented by the Macondo well.**

Observations

Summary Observation 5.1: **The ability of the oil and gas industry to perform and maintain an integrated assessment of the margins of safety for a complex well like Macondo is impacted by the complex structure of the offshore oil and gas industry and the divisions of technical expertise among the many contractors engaged in the drilling effort.**

Observation 5.2: **Processes within the oil and gas industry to assess adequately the integrated risks associated with drilling a deepwater well, such as Macondo, are currently lacking.**

Observation 5.3: **As offshore drilling extends into deeper water, its complexity increases. However, in-house technical capabilities within many operating companies for well drilling operations have diminished in favor of reliance on multiple contractors. This, in turn, diminishes the capacity of operations companies (the "operator") to assess and integrate the multiplicity of factors potentially affecting the safety of the well.**

Observation 5.4: **The operating leaseholder company is the only entity involved in offshore drilling that is positioned to manage the overall system safety of well drilling and rig operations.**

The rapid evolution of deepwater drilling operations has challenged management of E&P companies to have in-house expertise in the complexities, risk, and system safety of deepwater operations and with monitoring capabilities for supporting the decision-making levels in a timely manner.

The operating company is typically recognized as the party responsible for the drilling and production of a well.[7,8] This is a long-term practice of leaseholders and, through a formal contract, all owners of the lease agree to authorize one of them as being the operator. The responsibility of the designated operator is to conduct a safe operation. This responsibility requires that the operator have the capacity to understand the complexities of the system safety issues and the ability to integrate these issues into coherent and executable operations.

Education, Training, and Certification of Personnel Involved with Offshore Drilling

During the mergers and consolidations in the 1990s, E&P companies saw that the service sector and contractors could provide much of the required expertise and that the companies could downsize their technical staffs and R&D organizations. This change in philosophy by the operating companies had the effect of converting experienced and trained personnel into outside consultants working for service and contracting companies. In essence, much of the in-house expertise was transferred out of the E&P companies, which made the standardization and easy coordination of safety and operational training almost impossible.

As the E&P industry moved toward greater reliance on contractors, consultants, and service company support, a major challenge arose for operators: assessing the experience levels, training, and ability of the personnel to execute an integrated safety program for an offshore drilling operation.

Training requirements, including those for well control, vary among companies. While many companies outsourced all of their training, others attempted to provide in-house well control training.

Because contractor personnel control subsea systems, they have become the implementers of well control. However, knowledge of geological conditions and well architecture resides in the operating companies. Such a divergence presents the need for team integration, but rig crews tend not to be trained as a team for activities such as well control, subsea problem solving, and other safety issues. Team exercises for emergencies tend to consist mainly of periodic drills to muster at lifeboat stations, which leaves much uncertainty as to how the crew will respond in an emergency.

Also, there is a need to educate technical and managerial personnel in system risk assessment and management. In its accident investigation report, BP indicated that "a formal risk assessment might have enabled the BP Macondo well team to identify further mitigation options to address risks" with respect to

---

[7]Report of the Society of Petroleum Engineers Gulf of Mexico Deepwater Drilling and Completions Advisory Summit to NAE/NRC Committee, March 2011, http://www. spe.org/industry/docs/SPESpillSummit.pdf. Most recently accessed Jan. 17, 2012.

[8]Responses of International Association of Drilling Contractors to questions from the committee, March 2011.

cementing the well during the temporary abandonment process (BP 2010, 34). More broadly, no evidence was found to indicate that any of the critical operational decisions made while drilling the Macondo well were subjected to a formal risk assessment process (BOEMRE 2011; Presidential Commission 2011).

> *Summary Observation 5.5:* **The extent of industry training of key personnel and decision makers has been inconsistent with the complexities and risks of deepwater drilling.**

> *Observation 5.6:* **There are too few standardized requirements across companies for education, training, and certification of personnel involved in deepwater drilling.**

Near-Miss Information

Gathering and disseminating near-miss information can play an important role in avoiding accidents. Worldwide, governments have different requirements for recording and retaining drilling information, including near-miss well-control incidents. Current and past efforts in the United States to collect and disseminate relevant data on well drilling generally rely on the mandatory reporting of accidents resulting in pollution events, injuries, or fatalities. There is no program analogous to the Aviation Safety Reporting System (ASRS) in U.S. civil aviation, which allows airline pilots and other crew members to provide near-miss information on a confidential basis. ASRS, which is based on voluntary reporting and is administered by the National Aeronautics and Space Administration, analyzes the information and makes it available to the public and across the aviation industry for educational purposes to lessen the likelihood of aviation incidents and accidents.

For years, companies and contractors in the oil and gas industry have collected drilling data on all offshore wells. Information on kicks, well pressures, and other aspects of wells is included. Shell, Statoil, and several other companies have developed real-time drilling monitoring centers to collect that information, and on-shore personnel oversee the data streams. The sophistication of these centers varies, and how the data are used differs from company to company. However, many offshore operations do not have real-time monitoring centers.

In a report from the Society of Petroleum Engineers, members indicated that the drilling industry is generally not willing to "publicly share information about all errors, omissions, and questionable results because of the potential for liability, legal partner issues, competitive pressures, and unpredictability of court rulings and public interpretation".[9] According to members of the International Association of Drilling Contractors, so long as legal liabilities exist, it is unlikely that efforts to share near-miss information across companies will be fruitful.[10]

> **Summary Observation 5.7:** **Overall, the companies involved have not made effective use of real-time data analysis, information on precursor incidents or near misses, or lessons learned in the Gulf of Mexico and worldwide to adjust practices and standards appropriately.**

Research and Development

For decades, a significant majority of R&D investments were made by individual oil and gas companies. However, about 20 years ago, as deepwater exploration and development was evolving into a major activity in the Gulf of Mexico, many companies were reducing R&D spending (NPC 2006). The move to outsource R&D in general had begun. The research that was being carried out had more to do with facilities and deepwater exploration, drilling, and production technologies than with system safety. R&D focused on system safety includes aspects such as better safety software, real-time data monitoring and interpretation, and systems simulations that could assess the risk levels of a given deepwater drilling system. R&D that is focused on system safety should also involve the ability to assess effects of environmental conditions on MODU operation, which includes the drilling unit.

> **Summary Observation 5.8:** **Industry's R&D efforts have been focused disproportionately on exploration, drilling, and production technologies as opposed to safety.**

RECOMMENDATIONS

Responsibility and Accountability

> **Summary Recommendation 5.1:** **Operating companies should have ultimate responsibility and accountability for well integrity, because only they are in a position to have visibility into all its aspects. Operating companies should be held responsible and accountable for well design, well construction, and the suitability of the rig and associated**

---

[9]Report of the Society of Petroleum Engineers Gulf of Mexico Deepwater Drilling and Completions Advisory Summit to NAE/NRC Committee, March 2011, http://www.spe.org/industry/docs/SPESpillSummit.pdf. Most recently accessed Jan. 17, 2012.

[10]Responses of the International Association of Drilling Contractors to questions from the committee, March 2011.

safety equipment. **Notwithstanding the above, the drilling contractor should be held responsible and accountable for the operation and safety of the offshore equipment.**[11]

> **Recommendation 5.1a: Coordination of multiple contractors should be reinforced to maintain a common focus on overall safety.**

> **Recommendation 5.1b: Operating companies should develop and maintain the proper oversight of contractor work.**

The operating company assumes the responsibility for (*a*) understanding the environment of well drilling, including characteristics of the marine surface, subsurface, seafloor, and local weather; (*b*) selecting the equipment to drill a well and ensuring that it is safe, reliable, certified, and capable of executing the well drilling program; (*c*) creating the well design and a program that adheres to safety standards; and (*d*) managing all the parties involved in executing the well plan. Because offshore operations require a high level of technical competencies, any organization that would assume the role of operator needs to have the readily available and internal capacity to be able to access the technical and operational competencies of the contractors and service providers.

However, drilling contractors (being the operators of the MODU and the drilling equipment) have the duty of ensuring that their equipment and personnel are capable of executing a well plan and that personnel are properly trained and certified.

Operating companies generally rely on one of their representatives, often referred to as "the company man" (or more formally as the well site leader), to coordinate all of the contractors and to have responsibility for the drilling activities. It is important that a system be in place allowing—before changes in the shifts of the company man—an appropriate transition of knowledge, information, and responsibilities concerning the coordination of the contractors and activities.

Research and Development

> **Summary Recommendation 5.2: Industry should greatly expand R&D efforts focused on improving the overall safety of offshore drilling in the areas of design, testing, modeling, risk assessment, safety culture, and systems integration. Such efforts should encompass well design, drilling and marine equipment, human factors, and management systems. These endeavors should be conducted to benefit the efforts of industry and government to instill a culture of safety.**

---

[11]This recommendation is also presented in Chapter 6 as Recommendation 6.20.

Some R&D for general safety that is not necessarily tied into specific operating companies can be done by outside organizations. The Electric Power Research Institute (EPRI)[12] and SINTEF[13] provide possible analogs of how outside organizations can successfully contribute to safety improvement in industry. Creation of industry, academic, and government consortia and collaborative R&D centers of excellence can also significantly contribute to accomplishment of this goal.

As research efforts focused on the safety of offshore drilling operations have been relegated to manufacturers, contractors, and service providers, much less of that research is done by the operators. Furthermore, there is little coordination of system safety research associated with offshore drilling operations. Improved approaches are needed for assessing various safety-related scenarios and the associated risk levels *before* the occurrence of a relevant incident. Industrywide standards should be developed for quantitative risk assessment to be used explicitly as a management tool for evaluating the risks of alternative choices.

Education and Training

Summary Recommendation 5.3: **Industry should undertake efforts to expand significantly the formal education and training of industry personnel engaged in offshore drilling to support proper implementation of system safety.**

Recommendation 5.3a: **Education of rig personnel early in their careers can be provided through a system similar to community or technical colleges.**

Recommendation 5.3b: **In addition to rig personnel, onshore personnel involved in overseeing or supporting rig-based operations should have sufficient understanding of the fundamental processes and risks involved.**

---

[12]EPRI is an independent company that conducts R&D relating to the generation, delivery, and use of electricity for the benefit of the public. For example, EPRI's Risk and Safety Management Program conducts research for the development of a risk-informed framework for nuclear power plants. http://portfolio.epri.com/default.aspx. Most recently accessed Jan. 17, 2012.

[13]SINTEF (Stiftelsen for Industriell og Teknisk Forskning) is an independent research organization based in Scandinavia that conducts research on technology, medicine, and the social sciences. One of SINTEF's primary objectives is to provide a better in-depth understanding of how to assess, monitor, and control safety and reliability. http://www.sintef.no/home/. Most recently accessed Jan. 17, 2012.

Recommendation 5.3c: **A research process is needed for establishing standardized requirements for education, training, and certification of everyone working on an offshore drilling rig. Additional standardized requirements should be established for education, training, and certification of key drilling-related personnel working offshore and onshore.**

Specific education for drilling operations, especially offshore drilling, is lacking. There are a variety of related engineering disciplines such as petroleum, mechanical, chemical, and industrial engineering, but only a few programs offer introductory courses in drilling. Therefore, individuals receive training in drilling engineering through programs designed within a company, which generally include some type of apprenticeship program providing drilling experience under the oversight of experienced drilling personnel. Offshore drilling engineering tends to rely on principles developed for onshore operations while gaining experience from offshore operations. Some offshore drilling engineers working for contractors change roles and work for operators.

Drilling personnel come from all walks of life. They usually start in the onshore drilling industry, learning by experience with hardly any formal education in key areas such as the overall drilling system, geology, fluid flow, and chemistry. Offshore drilling personnel can be recruited from a variety of institutions and organizations, including technical schools and general colleges, and from those with specialized naval backgrounds. Few recruits are likely to have even a fundamental understanding of the overall drilling system and the environment into which the system is deployed. Training is mostly done by contractors and is focused on a specific job. There are commercial organizations that provide required training, such as for well control and survival (e.g., helicopter underwater egress training), but little else. Different companies have training and career paths that vary greatly. There are few industry standards for the level of education and training required for a particular job in drilling.

Incident Reporting Systems

Summary Recommendation 5.4: **Industry and regulators should improve corporate and industrywide systems for reporting safety-related incidents. Reporting should be facilitated by enabling anonymous or "safety privileged" inputs. Corporations should investigate all such reports and disseminate their lessons-learned findings in a timely manner to all their operating and decision-making personnel and to the industry as a whole. A comprehensive lessons-learned repository should be maintained for industrywide use. This information can be used for training in accident prevention and continually improving standards.**[14]

---

[14]This recommendation is also presented in Chapter 6 as Recommendation 6.14.

Thousands of offshore wells have been drilled, some with extreme difficulty. However, information on near misses or the events that might have caused near misses is rarely exchanged through the trade literature or professional meetings. The committee is unaware of any publicly available database on near misses and their causes, specifically for the Gulf of Mexico. There appears to be an industrywide reluctance to disseminate information on such events; most companies retain the information for internal use, except when they are required to reveal it.

Fostering Safety Culture

Summary Recommendation 5.5: Industry should foster an effective safety culture through consistent training, adherence to principles of human factors, system safety, and continued measurement through leading indicators.

Leading indicators provide ongoing assurance that risks are being adequately controlled. An example of a leading indicator would be a measure of preparedness to manage an emergency situation. One component of that measure would be the training sessions conducted by an offshore team. [See HSE (2006) and OECD (2008) for other examples.]

> *Recommendation 5.5a:* **The committee endorses the concept of a "center for offshore safety" to train, monitor the work experience of, and certify (license) personnel. Leadership of the center should involve persons affiliated with one or more neutral organizations that are outside of the petroleum industry.**

> *Recommendation 5.5b:* **Effective response to a crisis situation requires teamwork to share information and perform actions. Training should involve on-site team exercises to develop competent decision making, coordination, and communication. Emergency team drills should involve full participation, as would be required in actual emergency situations, including a well blowout. Companies should approach team training as a means of instilling overall safety as a high priority.**

> *Recommendation 5.5c:* **Use of training simulators similar to those applied in the aerospace industry and the military should be considered. Approaches using simulators should include team training for coordination of activities in crisis situations.**

Each operating company, service provider, and drilling contractor has been viewed by the oil and gas industry as responsible for its own training.

Training in such areas as well control and survival in harsh environments could be obtained from a variety of sources with certified training programs.

Each company, whether an operator or contractor, specifies its level of training and experience for a particular job function and how much training per year is required. There is little industrywide uniformity in the amount or the type of training required for a particular job. Testing after training has not been standardized, nor has follow-up to assess competency levels. Overall, in the drilling industry there is little uniformity in the type, amount, and frequency of training. Furthermore, there is a noticeable lack of team training and training of management personnel who make critical decisions for offshore drilling operations. (See recommendations in Chapter 4 on education and training of rig personnel.)

Capping and Containment Systems

Summary Recommendation 5.6: **Efforts to reduce the probability of future blowouts should be complemented by capabilities of mitigating the consequences of a loss of well control. Industry should ensure timely access to demonstrated well-capping and containment capabilities.**

The Macondo well–*Deepwater Horizon* event, in which the BOP system failed to contain the hydrocarbons that escaped thousands of feet below the surface of the water, presented a challenge to the offshore industry as a whole that it was not immediately prepared to address. No primary well containment system was available. The operator was compelled to use what equipment was readily obtainable in or near the Gulf of Mexico and to adapt various makeshift designs (on the basis of trial and error) of risers, caps, and other equipment to contain the hydrocarbon flow, direct it to floating production facilities, and eventually stop the flow out of the well. This process took months, during which millions of barrels of hydrocarbons flowed into the gulf waters. The incident dramatically showed the vulnerability of subsea BOP systems. Therefore, access to a containment system that can be rapidly deployed to a well is an essential aspect for offshore drilling in the near future while BOP system reliability is improved.

The committee endorses industry's recent initiatives to establish highly capable containment systems in the event of future well blowouts. One such initiative is the well containment response system developed by the Helix Well Containment Group,[15] which is a consortium of deepwater operating companies in the Gulf of Mexico with the objective of expanding capabilities to respond to a subsea spill. Each member company contributes expertise and resources to help the group develop the capability of rapid intervention, response, and containment. This system is now operational.

---

[15] http://www.hwcg.org/. Most recently accessed Jan. 17, 2012.

Also, the Marine Well Containment Company is an organization set up for the purpose of containing an underwater well control incident in U.S. Gulf of Mexico. Membership is open to all oil and gas operators in the U.S. gulf waters, and the group is funding and building a containment system intended to be more flexible than the Helix system. It will be compatible with a wide range of well designs and equipment, oil and natural gas flow rates, and weather conditions.[16]

Industry or other organizations should support the further development of containment systems with R&D efforts, field tests, risk analysis, simulations, and so forth to improve preparedness, reliability, and the effectiveness of future containment.

---

[16]http://www.marinewellcontainment.com/index.php. Most recently accessed Jan. 17, 2012.

6

Regulatory Reform

Offshore oil and gas exploration and production are inherently hazardous activities requiring the coordinated utilization of many complex systems by hundreds of people working for dozens of companies. Hazards associated with offshore drilling operations arise from a variety of activities and factors. As indicated in Chapter 5, some hazards can lead to accidents on the scale of individual workers and are in the realm of *occupational safety*. In contrast, *system safety*[1] refers to offshore drilling hazards that can lead to accidents on a much larger scale, involving multiple fatalities, substantial property loss, and extensive environmental damage. Given the charge to the committee, this chapter focuses on regulatory reform related to improving system safety.

The Minerals Management Service (MMS) of the U.S. Department of the Interior (DOI) was the federal agency primarily responsible for regulating the safety of offshore drilling at the time of the Macondo well–*Deepwater Horizon* incident. After the incident, the newly formed Bureau of Ocean Energy Management, Regulation, and Enforcement (BOEMRE)[2] was assigned responsibility for regulating the safety of offshore drilling operations previously assigned to MMS. As reorganizations continued within DOI, BOEMRE split into two entities on October 1, 2011. Currently, the Bureau of Safety and Environmental Enforcement (BSEE) is the federal entity responsible for safety and environmental oversight of offshore oil and gas operations. Several other agencies, such as the U.S. Coast Guard, also play important regulatory roles. The regulatory authorities sometimes overlap, and specific agreements between agencies are used in some cases to define regulatory jurisdictions.

Since the Macondo well–*Deepwater Horizon* incident, DOI has undertaken several actions to improve the safety of and reduce risks associated with offshore oil and gas activities. This chapter considers efforts intended to shift the

---

[1] In some industries (e.g., chemical) the term *process safety* is also used.

[2] On May 19, 2010, Interior Secretary Salazar issued Secretarial Order No. 3299, which restructured MMS by reassigning its responsibilities to two newly formed bureaus. The bureau eventually named the Bureau of Ocean Energy Management, Regulation, and Enforcement was assigned responsibility for regulating the safety of offshore drilling operations.

regulatory system for deepwater drilling from reliance on mainly prescriptive regulations to performance-based regulations that specify safety goals to be achieved by the regulated organizations, as discussed below. The chapter also provides recommendations for enhancing the regulatory reform that is now under way. The recommendations were developed to address needs identified during presentations to the committee, in previously published reports (such as Presidential Commission 2011), and the committee's evaluation of regulatory systems for offshore drilling in the Gulf of Mexico and other locations (e.g., the North Sea).

REGULATION OF U.S. OFFSHORE DRILLING BEFORE THE MACONDO WELL BLOWOUT

MMS had relied on a primarily prescriptive approach for regulation of offshore drilling. Under that approach, specific requirements for equipment and operations were developed, and then compliance with the regulations was monitored through auditing. Prescriptive regulations are often developed through a multiyear process in response to events or observed trends. As a result, the regulations invariably are neither timely nor complete and lag behind the development of new technologies.[3]

Over the past few decades, exploration and production companies within the oil and gas industry developed advanced technology that led to a marked increase in deepwater drilling in the Gulf of Mexico. During that period, the predominantly prescriptive regulatory system for deepwater drilling used by MMS did not keep up with these technological advances. It became more problematic because its level of funding and technical staffing remained static or decreased as industry's offshore drilling activity increased. Furthermore, the distribution of those limited resources among MMS regions was not aligned with the relative amounts of offshore industrial activity in the regions. The Pacific region, with about one MMS inspector for every five offshore facilities, was more fully staffed and equipped than were the Gulf of Mexico regions, which employed about one inspector for every 54 facilities (DOI 2010b).

As discussed previously in this report, the Macondo well blowout was precipitated by multiple flawed decisions involving the operator, drilling contractor, and service companies as they moved toward temporary abandonment of the well despite indications of increasing hazard. The net effect of these decisions made by the rig personnel was to reduce the available margins of safety that take into account complexities of the hydrocarbon reservoirs and well geology discovered through drilling and the subsequent changes in the execution of the well plan. Critical aspects of drilling operations were left to industry to de-

---

[3]A general discussion of federal regulation of offshore drilling in the United States with a focus on regulatory oversight of deepwater drilling in the Gulf of Mexico is provided by Presidential Commission (2011).

cide without MMS review of the effects of the changes on the overall risk with regard to the temporary abandonment procedures. For example, no person in authority from a regulatory agency was required to review critical test data from Macondo, such as the results of the negative pressure test. Had this been a requirement before operations could continue, it is possible that the test data would have exposed the fact that the hydrocarbon-producing formations had not been adequately isolated and were in communication with the well (see Chapter 2). Also, prior to the Macondo well blowout, there were numerous warnings to both the industry and regulators about potential failures of blowout preventer (BOP) systems widely in use. While the inadequacies were identified and documented in various reports over the years, it appears that there was a misplaced trust by both industry and responsible government authorities in the ability of the BOP to act as a fail-safe mechanism (see Chapter 3).

The National Commission on the BP *Deepwater Horizon* Oil Spill and Offshore Drilling found that MMS regulations were inadequate to address the risks of deepwater drilling and did not assess the full set of risks presented by the temporary abandonment procedure used at the Macondo well. The commission's report also noted that MMS lacked sufficient personnel with the expertise and training needed to enforce those regulations effectively and to supplement the regulations by appropriately assessing the procedure's safety (Presidential Commission 2011). In its report concerning the causes of the *Deepwater Horizon*–Macondo well incident, BOEMRE concluded that at the time of the blowout, MMS did not have a comprehensive set of regulations specifically addressing deepwater technology, drilling, or well design. Had improved regulations been in effect at the time, they may have decreased the likelihood of the Macondo blowout (BOEMRE 2011).[4,5]

On the basis of its review of the regulatory scheme in place at the time of the Macondo well blowout and the chronology of events leading up to the incident, the committee presents the following observations:

Summary Observation 6.1: **The regulatory regime was ineffective in addressing the risks of the Macondo well. The actions of the regulators did not display an awareness of the risks or the very narrow margins of safety.**

Summary Observation 6.2: **The extent of training of key personnel and decision makers in regulatory agencies has been inconsistent with the complexities and risks of deepwater drilling.**

---

[4]The BOEMRE report describes various regulatory approvals provided by MMS prior to the blowout.

[5]The BOEMRE report also indicates that the BOEMRE panel found evidence that parties involved in drilling the Macondo well violated federal regulations in place at the time of the blowout.

Summary Observation 6.3: **Overall, the regulatory community has not made effective use of real-time data analysis, information on precursor incidents or near misses, or lessons learned in the Gulf of Mexico and worldwide to adjust practices and standards appropriately.**

For example, MMS last produced an analysis of offshore incidents for calendar year 2000 (Presidential Commission 2011).

DOI'S SAFETY AND ENVIRONMENTAL MANAGEMENT SYSTEMS

The *Deepwater Horizon*–Macondo well incident, like major offshore accidents in other countries, demonstrated the need for a proactive systems safety approach integrating all aspects of drilling operations that could affect occupational and system safety. In this regard, the committee commends DOI for instituting Safety and Environmental Management Systems (SEMS) in 30 CFR 250 (*Federal Register*, Vol. 75, No. 199, Oct. 15, 2010). Implementation of SEMS began on November 15, 2011.

SEMS is a proactive, goal-oriented risk management system similar in many ways to the systems used in the North Sea by the United Kingdom and Norway and on the outer continental shelves of Canada and Australia. SEMS requires companies to develop, implement, and manage a safety and environmental management system in accordance with the American Petroleum Institute's (API's) Recommended Practice 75 for Development of a Safety and Environmental Management Program for Offshore Operations and Facilities. The committee sees this development as an important step toward achieving comprehensive reform of the regulatory processes governing offshore drilling activities in U.S. waters.

The following are advantages of goal-setting risk management systems over prescriptive regulatory systems:

- Putting the focus on achieving clearly stated health, safety, and environmental objectives;
- Requiring operators, drilling contractors, and service companies to document their approach to safety, in contrast to basing safety on compliance with prescriptive regulations;
- Requiring operators, drilling contractors, and service companies to work together to meet safety objectives;
- Formalizing and documenting the risk management procedures and responsibilities of all parties;
- Providing a context for effective communication on health, safety, and environmental issues as they arise;
- Providing for checks and balances for well planning and operations, especially with regard to management of change;

- Allowing for the health, safety, and environmental procedures and policies of all participating companies to be incorporated into a unified health, safety, and environmental plan;
- Providing the opportunity for independent assessment of well planning, drilling, and related operations and overall conformance to stated goals for health, safety, and environmental protection;
- Providing a cost–effective approach to regulating the evolving technology employed by the offshore oil and gas industry, enabling a reduction in prescriptive regulations, and
- Potentially reducing the cost of compliance for companies already familiar with similar approaches used elsewhere in the world.

While the committee strongly endorses the actions of DOI in establishing the SEMS requirements, it sees this as a first step in a long process toward achieving the capabilities required of an appropriate regulatory system for offshore drilling in the United States. An appropriate regulatory system should have the following characteristics:

- Be effective in regulating both high-risk, high-consequence wells, such as those in deep water or those likely to encounter very high pore pressures, and relatively low-risk wells, such as infill wells in relatively shallow water.[6] Provide a mechanism allowing the government to assess the risks (and the measures proposed for managing those risks) associated with the proposed well plan and a way for the government to assess the competence of the companies and individuals to be involved in carrying out the proposed drilling activities.
- Incorporate a formal management of change process that would allow well plans and procedures to adapt to uncertainties in geology and pore pressure, to changing weather conditions, and to other factors, while keeping parties informed of ongoing changes.
- Work effectively with the structure of the U.S. offshore oil and gas industry. Encourage the development and integration of a strong safety culture and safety management systems among operating companies (and joint venture partner companies), drilling contractors, and service companies.
- Ensure that all drilling activities are conducted with risks reduced as low as reasonably practical.
- Motivate industry to invest in technologies and processes that will further minimize risk.

No regulatory system will, by itself, ensure safe drilling operations. What is most important is that every company involved—including operators and

---

[6]Infill wells are new wells that are drilled within the original well pattern of a development area. Because a number of wells have already been drilled in the area, a great deal is known about optimal drilling procedures.

partner companies, drilling contractors, and equipment and service providers—develop, promote, and operate in a system safety culture embraced by top management and implemented in every phase of drilling operations. No matter what regulatory system is used, safe operations ultimately depend on the commitment to system safety by the people involved at all levels within the organization.

GOAL-ORIENTED RISK MANAGEMENT REGULATORY SYSTEMS

Until recently, the United States depended on a primarily prescriptive regulatory system in which operators were required to demonstrate conformance with established regulations. Other countries used similar prescriptive regulatory systems until a series of accidents indicated the need to adopt a proactive, goal-oriented risk management system similar to the one recommended here. The precipitating events for a major change of the Norwegian regulatory system were several serious accidents over an 11-year period. Among them were the blowout on the Bravo platform in the Ekofisk field in 1977 and the capsizing of the *Alexander L. Kielland*, a ship used as a floating hotel for Ekofisk workers, in 1980 (killing 123 of 212 people on board). Similarly, the United Kingdom and Canada were led to abandon their prescriptive regulatory approach and adopt a more proactive, goal-oriented approach to system safety by, respectively, the explosions and fire aboard the *Piper Alpha* production platform off Scotland in 1988 (killing 167 workers) and the sinking of the *Ocean Ranger* semisubmersible drilling platform off Newfoundland in 1982 (killing all 84 crew members). An important attribute of goal-oriented risk management systems is that they provide a greater opportunity for the adoption of new technology as it becomes available. For example, both in U.S. waters and abroad, several of the operating companies are using shore-based real-time operations centers to monitor offshore drilling operations continuously, although there is no explicit requirement to do so.

Goal-oriented risk-management systems require that companies responsible for compliance demonstrate to regulators that procedures for health, safety, and environmental protection are in place to achieve explicitly stated safety goals to prevent and respond effectively to all conceivable accidents. Consideration is given to elements such as redundant barriers (designed to minimize the likelihood of accidents) and controls (designed to provide detailed plans, procedures, and facilities for responding to accidents should they occur). In addition, industry demonstrates that its management system ensures that its personnel always have the qualifications and training necessary for performing their duties in a safe manner.

Three fundamental strategies are employed in goal-oriented risk management systems to deal with drilling and safety systems: reduce the likelihood of malfunctions in system components, reduce the effects of malfunctions should they occur, and increase the detection and correction of malfunctions in system components. Different methods can be employed in the context of these three strategies to enable the designated "acceptable risks" (the explicit goals) to be realized.

Implementation Aspects of a Goal-Oriented Risk Management System

Consideration of some specifics will help in understanding how goal-oriented risk management systems work. First, instead of listing explicit regulations, such systems principally rely on meeting functional safety requirements through utilization of equipment and procedures that conform with explicit standards, guidelines, and best practice documents. In Norway, the Petroleum Safety Authority (PSA) retains a limited number of explicit regulations but primarily relies on guidelines associated with international codes and standards (including some specific to the European Union) and specially developed national (NORSOK) standards to define best practices as applied to different systems. For example, NORSOK D-010 lists standards for well integrity, BOP testing, cementing, and so forth, whereas NORSOK 001 applies to drilling equipment. In addition, the drilling contractor must obtain an "acknowledgment of compliance" (AoC) covering its equipment, personnel, and safety management systems. In Norway these codes and standards are considered "living documents" with frequent reviews and updates resulting from consultation between industry and regulators.

Finally, while a fundamental aspect of the Norwegian regulatory system is a high degree of dialogue, consensus, and trust between operating companies and regulators, PSA carries out *drop-in* audits of offshore operations utilizing its own personnel, experts from SINTEF (Stiftelsen for Industriell og Teknisk Forskning, an independent research organization), and other outside experts. If it determines that the company does not have sufficient expertise to carry out the proposed drilling plan, PSA *withholds consent* for an operator's plan. Drilling operations are not allowed to proceed until PSA consents. The regulatory approaches used by the United Kingdom and Norway in the North Sea have been tailored to the structure of their governments, local industry, and labor. Applying the concept of goal-oriented risk management to the Gulf of Mexico will require similar tailoring. However, many of the concepts and documents used for the North Sea can provide valuable templates for a system structured for the United States. In addition, both the United Kingdom (HSE 2011) and Norway (PSA 2011a) have extensive, long-term R&D efforts that help industry and government regulators advance technology, management, and governance to meet current operational requirements.

Tools for Clarifying the Roles Among Companies Within a Goal-Oriented Risk Management System

The basic planning documents of a goal-oriented risk management system are the risk management plans of the drilling contractor, operator, and service companies. The committee supports the concept of a project-specific *bridging* document for use in the United States that integrates the risk management plans of all parties involved in a given project. API and the International Association of Drilling Contractors are developing a Well Construction Interface Document that could be a model for such a bridging document. Several advantages of using a bridging document as part of a goal-oriented risk management system are that it could help

*   Unify the risk management systems of the operator, drilling contractor, and service companies in a way that clearly defines the roles and responsibilities of all parties for health, safety, and environmental protection;
*   Provide detailed project-specific information to be shared by key personnel regardless of whether they are employed by the operator, the drilling contractor, or a service company; and
*   Facilitate the management of change process and serve as a mechanism to communicate the implications of program changes to all key personnel.

Offshore drilling in U.S. waters is frequently done by a group of partner companies, who jointly own the lease. Through a joint operating agreement, the partner companies stipulate who the *operating* company will be (usually this is the company with majority interest) and the financial terms and responsibilities that govern the partnership. The operating company is recognized to have the principal responsibility for compliance with rules and regulations governing offshore operations, but the partner companies (as co-lease holders) should have a "see to" responsibility to ensure that the operator conducts activities in such a manner that risk is *as low as reasonably practicable*, which has a legislative and legal base and provides the strength for regulatory–governance enforcement. Such shared responsibilities should be clearly spelled out in the oil and gas lease agreements administered by DOI as well as in the joint operating agreement among the partner companies.

A Hybrid Goal-Oriented Risk Management System

Well construction and abandonment operations include safety-critical points at which faulty decisions would likely result in a substantial increase in hazard. Examples are casing and cementing operations (which would encompass reviewing cement bond logs and formation integrity tests) and the establishment and testing of multiple barriers to flow before temporary or permanent well abandonment. A hybrid regulatory approach—expanding on the SEMS goal-oriented safety system with requirements for explicit regulatory review and approval of the safety-critical points before operations can proceed—would help guard against faulty decisions being made. This expansion of SEMS is analogous to adding the inspection and *sign-off* process associated with routine construction projects and is the standard practice of the Bureau of Land Management during its regulation of onshore drilling for oil and gas on federal lands.

Similarly, when operating conditions are hazardous, regulatory approval for operations to proceed should be required. This could occur, for example when the difference between the equivalent circulating density and the fracture gradient is not greater than a predefined minimum value either during drilling or cementing.

Offshore drilling operations will face increasing complexity as they move into ever-greater water depths and more challenging environments. In some cases, complex operations may require a *process of continual problem-solving.* For operations to proceed safely and efficiently in challenging environments, it is essential for private industry and BSEE to collaborate in developing a list of safety-critical points and in establishing safe operating limits. It is also critical that BSEE have knowledgeable personnel in place to provide meaningful reviews. The requirements for regulatory review and approval should not deter operating companies from developing comprehensive risk assessment systems with clearly stated goals.

Barriers to Implementation

A number of the companies operating in the Gulf of Mexico use proactive risk management systems in foreign countries where they have been operating for many years. These systems address operational safety through the full life cycle of drilling and well completion activities. Some oil and gas companies already use risk management systems similar to SEMS when they carry out deepwater drilling in the Gulf of Mexico for internal project management. However, the committee recognizes that use of a new regulatory system for offshore drilling risk management will place new demands on both private industry and BSEE. In the long term the costs of compliance under the system would likely be less than those of complying with increasing amounts of prescriptive regulations. More important, an effective regulatory system has the potential to reduce the extraordinary costs associated with catastrophic accidents such as those associated with the Macondo well. Given that the disaster might have been avoided had improved regulations been in place, the potential benefits of an effective regulatory system are self-evident.

Offshore drilling in U.S. waters has a unique history, culture, and suite of business practices. SEMS will require new ways of thinking (and a new mode of interaction) between the oil and gas industry companies, contractors, and service companies on the one hand and BSEE and other U.S. regulatory agencies on the other. SEMS will require companies to adopt both a *top-down* and a *bottom-up* safety culture. Safe drilling operations cannot be achieved solely through regulations, inspections, or mandates. They will only be realized when there is a full commitment to system safety, from the board room to the rig floor, and through recognition that a focus only on occupational safety will not ensure system safety. Compliance with either prescriptive regulations or standards related to achieving specific safety goals need to be considered a minimum requirement and not necessarily a way to meet duty of care obligations.

The use of SEMS will require increased competence of everyone involved in offshore drilling operations—from the engineers developing technical plans and the workers and technicians carrying them out to the regulators overseeing such operations. As discussed in Chapter 5, there is a need for a better-educated and better-trained work force in the United States to avoid catastrophic system failures and meet the challenges of the future. This need includes a better-educated and better-trained regulatory workforce.

RECOMMENDATIONS

Regulatory Development and Implementation

Summary Recommendation 6.1: **The United States should fully implement a hybrid regulatory system that incorporates a limited number of prescriptive elements into a proactive, goal-oriented risk management system for health, safety, and the environment.**

Recommendation 6.2: **BSEE should continue to work closely with private industry and other agencies in adopting and developing comprehensive goals and standards to govern the many processes and systems involved in offshore drilling.**

The emphasis of these goals and standards should not be to develop new regulations and requirements. Instead, they should provide a foundation for implementation of a proactive, interactive, and reactive risk management system by BSEE for drilling in U.S. waters.

Recommendation 6.3: **BSEE should make effective use of existing industry standards, well-established international standards, and best practice guidelines used by other countries, but it should recognize that standards need to be updated and revised continually.**

The standards should be forward looking and not only incorporate the many lessons learned from the Macondo well–*Deepwater Horizon* accident but also strive to identify potential problems in future drilling projects.

Recommendation 6.4: **As the SEMS program moves forward in the United States, BSEE should incorporate the steps already taken by private industry (and industry associations and consortia) to improve offshore drilling safety after the *Deepwater Horizon* accident.**

As discussed in Chapter 5, these steps include the development of several well containment corporations to enable member companies to access a wide array of equipment and personnel to minimize the environmental impact of drilling-related accidents and oil spills, should they occur. Another industry-led advance has been the Center for Offshore Safety. This center has the potential to engage the CEOs of oil and gas companies, drilling contractors, and service companies in risk management; set standards for training and certification; develop accreditation systems for industry training programs; and facilitate industry participation in safety audits and inspections. Ideally, the center should represent a collaboration of industry and government.

Recommendation 6.5: **Quantitative risk analysis should be an essential part of goal-oriented risk management systems.**

This formalism achieves several purposes. First, it provides a check that the risk (defined in quantitative terms) is tolerable. If the risk cannot be tolerated, it will define the adoption of measures, in the right order of priorities, to lower the risk. Second, it can be used to support decisions based on risk management models that individual companies currently use. Several oil companies already have sophistication in this area; quantitative risk analysis is used in exploration, portfolio management, and well design. It also important to ensure that caution and expert judgment are exercised to guard against the use of flawed data. In addition, those who perform the analyses should be able to communicate the results effectively for operational and management implementation.

Summary Recommendation 6.6: **BSEE and other regulators should identify and enforce safety-critical points during well construction and abandonment that warrant explicit regulatory review and approval before operations can proceed.**

Recommendation 6.7: **To augment SEMS, BSEE should work closely with private industry to develop a list of safety-critical points during well construction and abandonment that will require explicit regulatory review and approval before operations can proceed.**

Examples are casing and cementing operations (which would encompass reviewing cement bond logs and formation integrity tests) and the establishment and testing of multiple barriers to flow before temporary or permanent well abandonment.

Recommendation 6.8: **As part of a hybrid risk management system, BSEE should establish safe operating limits, which, when exceeded, would require regulatory approval for operations to proceed.**

Operating limits and checks should be established as part of the operator's management program, which will be reviewed and audited by the regulator. Examples of safe operating limits are the functionality of safety-critical systems such as the BOP (see Chapter 3) and the difference between the equivalent circulating density and the fracture gradient not being greater than a certain minimum (either during drilling or cementing) (see Chapter 2). These operating limits should be established in collaboration with industry.

> ***Recommendation 6.9:*** **BSEE should incorporate requirements for approval and certification of key steps during well construction into codes and standards.**

> ***Recommendation 6.10:*** **BSEE should review existing codes and standards to determine which should be improved regarding requirements for (*a*) use of state-of-the-art technologies, especially in areas related to well construction, cementing, BOP functionality, and alarm and evacuation systems, among others, and (*b*) approval and certification incumbent to management of changes in original plans for well construction.**

> ***Recommendation 6.11:*** **The manner in which the above-mentioned codes and standards will be enforced should be specified by BSEE in the well plan submitted by operating companies for approval.**

> ***Recommendation 6.12:*** **BSEE should adopt a system of precertification of operators, contractors, and service companies before granting a drilling permit for especially challenging projects.**

The precertification process would evaluate the technical sophistication and capabilities of both equipment and personnel tasked with carrying out drilling-related activities in the severe conditions of the deepwater environment. Specific criteria should be developed for conducting the evaluation.

> ***Recommendation 6.13:*** **BSEE should consider the use of independent well examiners to help in reviewing well plans and in regularly monitoring ongoing activities during drilling, completion, and abandonment.**

Independent well examiners are currently used in the United Kingdom (HSE 2008) and can play a productive role in reviewing the design of the well and in regularly monitoring ongoing activities during drilling, completion, and abandonment. Independent well examiners and third-party classification societies, working under contract to BSEE, could be especially helpful in conducting independent audits. Ideally, the independent well examiners or classification societies should be involved in a given project from its inception, including review of the well plan, through final well completion or abandonment activities.

In using these entities, BSEE should take care not to abrogate its primary ultimate responsibility for regulation of offshore drilling. In the United Kingdom, the regulator periodically audits the well examination arrangements. In addition, BSEE should develop requirements for determining the competence of examiners and their independence from the operating company. BSEE should also identify responsibilities for developing well examination schemes, ensuring scheme effectiveness, and ensuring that appropriate actions are taken on recommendations made by the well examiner.

Near-Miss Reporting

Summary Recommendation 6.14: **Industry, BSEE, and other regulators should improve corporate and industrywide systems for reporting safety-related incidents. Reporting should be facilitated by enabling anonymous or "safety privileged" inputs. Corporations should investigate all such reports and disseminate their lessons-learned findings in a timely manner to all their operating and decision-making personnel and to the industry as a whole. A comprehensive lessons-learned repository should be maintained for industrywide use. This information can be used for training in accident prevention and continually improving standards.[7]**

As part of this process, near misses and accident precursors should be tracked as a way of supporting a proactive risk management system. Such a database would be invaluable in enabling regulators, companies, and employees to learn from these occurrences.

Integration of Regulatory Approaches

Summary Recommendation 6.15: **A single U.S. government agency should be designated with responsibility for ensuring an integrated approach for system safety for all offshore drilling activities.**

Recommendation 6.16: **As a first step, DOI should work with other departments and agencies with jurisdiction over some aspect of offshore drilling activities to simplify and streamline the regulatory process for drilling on the U.S. outer continental shelf.**

Offshore drilling operations are currently governed by a number of agencies with complementary and in some cases overlapping areas of statutory responsibility. Table 6-1 lists a number of the principal agencies that have jurisdiction over regulating various potential hazards related to offshore drilling.

---

[7]This recommendation is also presented in Chapter 5 as Recommendation 5.4.

As part of the process of regulatory reform that led Norway to change from a prescriptive to a risk management system (and that separated PSA from the Norwegian Petroleum Directorate), a concerted effort was made to streamline, simplify, and centralize regulatory authority. Modifying the regulatory system governing drilling operations will be most effective as part of an integrated system of reforms that involve many of the hazards and agencies shown in Table 6-1.

TABLE 6-1 Offshore Drilling Operations and Relevant Federal Agencies

Hazard	Agencies exercising some jurisdiction over preventive control measures[a]
Attack or terrorist activity	FAA, FBI, FS, TSA, USCG
Blowout (loss of well control)	EPA, BOEMRE, USCG
Explosion	FS, BOEMRE, USCG
Events from adjacent installations	BOEMRE
Epidemic or pandemic	CDC, USCG
Fire	FS, BOEMRE, USCG
Diving operations	BOEMRE, USCG
Dropped objects	FS, BOEMRE, USCG
Helicopter crash	FAA, USCG
Loss of stability	FS, USCG
Major mechanical failure	FS, USCG
Mooring or station keeping failure	FS, BOEMRE, USCG
Seismic activity	FS, BOEMRE, USCG
Ship collision	FS, USCG
Structural failure	FS, BOEMRE, USCG
Toxic release	EPA, FAA, FS, BOEMRE, USCG
Weather and storms	FS, BOEMRE, NOAA, USCG

[a]Does not include possible jurisdiction to conduct an investigation following incident.
Abbreviations: CDC, Centers for Disease Control and Prevention; EPA, Environmental Protection Agency; FAA, Federal Aviation Administration; FBI, Federal Bureau of Investigation; FS, Flag-State maritime authority; BOEMRE, Bureau of Ocean Energy Management, Regulation, and Enforcement; NOAA, National Oceanic and Atmospheric Administration; TSA, Transportation Security Administration; USCG, United States Coast Guard.
NOTE: As a result of the recent reorganization of BOEMRE, the Bureau of Safety and Environmental Enforcement is the successor organization with responsibility for enforcing safety and environmental regulations.
Source: International Association of Drilling Contractors (IADC)[8]. Reprinted with permission, IADC.

---

[8]Responses of IADC to questions from the committee, March 2011.

Recommendation 6.17: BSEE should work with other federal agencies to delegate supporting regulatory responsibilities and accountabilities for ensuring system safety, integrating all aspects of system safety for the parts of offshore drilling operations in which a particular agency is involved (Table 6-1). BSEE should strive to involve the domain expertise and core competencies of the other relevant agencies. BSEE should have purview over integrating regulation, inspection, and monitoring enforcement for all aspects of system safety for offshore drilling operations.

Recommendation 6.18: BSEE should work with other federal agencies to develop efficient and effective mechanisms for investigating future accidents and incidents.

Net Assessment of Risk

Recommendation 6.19: DOI should require BSEE to provide the Secretary of the Interior with a net assessment of the risks of future drilling activities so that such risks can be factored into decisions with regard to new leases. Focusing on system safety, the assessment should be a formal probabilistic risk analysis that evaluates risks associated with all operations having the potential for significant harm to individuals, environmental damage, or economic loss. The operations addressed by the assessment should include drilling and well construction, temporary well abandonment, oil and gas production, and eventual well abandonment.

Responsibility and Accountability

Summary Recommendation 6.20: Operating companies should have ultimate responsibility and accountability for well integrity, because only they are in a position to have visibility into all its aspects. Operating companies should be held responsible and accountable for well design, well construction, and the suitability of the rig and associated safety equipment. Notwithstanding the above, the drilling contractor should be held responsible and accountable for the operation and safety of the offshore equipment (see Chapter 5).[9]

Recommendation 6.21: In carrying out its regulatory responsibilities, BSEE should view operating companies as taking full responsibility for the safety of offshore equipment and its use.

---

[9]This recommendation is also presented in Chapter 5 as Recommendation 5.1.

This responsibility also encompasses the subsea equipment, including the BOP, used as critical control barriers. As part of the proactive risk management system recommended here, BSEE should ensure that drilling contractors are required to obtain an AoC covering their equipment, personnel, and safety management system. The AoC process is used by Norway's PSA to decide whether the agency has confidence that drilling activities can be carried out by using a particular mobile offshore drilling unit within the framework of the regulations (PSA, 2011b).

> *Recommendation 6.22:* **While the operating company is recognized to have the principal responsibility for compliance with rules and regulations governing offshore operations, BSEE should require the partner companies (as co-lease holders) to have a "see to" responsibility to ensure that the operator conducts activities in such a manner that risk is as low as reasonably practicable.**

Regulatory Personnel

> *Summary Recommendation 6.23:* **BSEE and other regulators should undertake efforts to expand significantly the formal education and training of regulatory personnel engaged in offshore drilling roles to support proper implementation of system safety.**

> *Recommendation 6.24:* **BSEE should exert every effort to recruit, develop, and retain experienced and capable technical experts with critical domain competencies.**

This is especially important in the context of the recently enacted SEMS risk management system and the recognition that drilling on the outer continental shelf will grow in complexity. BSEE should strive to increase its technical competencies across the wide spectrum of expertise involved in offshore oil and gas exploration, including areas such as well design, cementing, BOPs, and remotely operated underwater vehicles.

Safety Culture

> *Summary Recommendation 6.25:* **BSEE and other regulators should foster an effective safety culture through consistent training, adherence to principles of human factors, system safety, and continued measurement through leading indicators.**[10]

---

[10]As discussed in Chapter 5, leading indicators provide ongoing assurance that risks are being adequately controlled.

Recommendation 6.26: **As a regulator, BSEE should enhance its internal safety culture to provide a positive example to the drilling industry through its own actions and the priorities it establishes.**

7

Concluding Comments

The loss of control over the Macondo well initiated a tragedy of momentous consequences. Eleven workers lost their lives, and the environment and economy of the gulf region were damaged in ways that are still being assessed. Furthermore, the blowout and subsequent oil spill severely damaged public confidence in both the offshore oil and gas industry and the federal regulatory process. A concerted effort by all participants will be necessary to overcome the reputational damage caused by this event. As the nation struggles with the consequences of dependency on foreign oil, it is appropriate that the risks associated with the exploration for and production of oil be factored into political decisions on where, when, and how to drill. All participants in the industry and regulatory communities have an obligation (a) to ensure that such considerations reflect a factual assessment of the risks, not an emotional one, and (b) to do all that they can to minimize those risks through technology development, personnel training, and management systems. Neither objective is likely to be achieved if the risks and the responsibility for addressing them are not recognized and accepted.

Envisioning failure is key to the safe development and operation of systems, particularly systems that incorporate the complexity of a deepwater well. Risks must be recognized, quantified, and mitigated. Designers, developers, operators, and regulators must know and understand that the risks are real and conduct themselves accordingly. If they do not, they face the likelihood of dealing with the consequences of the risks. There is an old saying in the U.S. Navy that there are only two categories of ship captains—those who have run their ship aground and those who will—and captains who believe that they belong in a third category shortly find that they are part of the first!

Neither industry nor U.S. regulators appear to have foreseen the risks of a Macondo-scale event. Even after the Montara blowout in the West Timor Sea in August 2009, industry and regulators testified before Congress,[1] providing assurances concerning the safety of operations in the Gulf of Mexico and the ade-

---

[1] Senate Hearing 111-303, Nov. 19, 2009. http://www.gpo.gov/fdsys/pkg/CHRG-111shrg55331/html/CHRG-111shrg55331.htm. Most recently accessed Jan. 17, 2012.

quacy of the regulatory process. Similarly, the lack of adequate, previously planned capping and containment techniques evidences a failure to envision an incident of the type or magnitude experienced at Macondo.

Today, industry and the regulators are both stating their good intentions. Industry is investing significant resources in capping and containment systems, and regulators are making significant organizational and process changes. The question remains as to whether these efforts are a start toward recognition, acceptance, and active management of the risks inherent in offshore oil and gas development or whether they represent a transitory response. For the sake of those who work offshore, those who live near the Gulf of Mexico, and all those dependent on the U.S. economy, the committee fervently hopes that these efforts are sustained.

References

ABBREVIATIONS

ABS	America Bureau of Shipping
BOEMRE	Bureau of Ocean Energy Management, Regulation, and Enforcement
CAIB	*Columbia* Accident Investigation Board
CCPS	Center for Chemical Process Safety
CSB	U.S. Chemical Safety Board
DHSG	*Deepwater Horizon* Study Group
DoD	U.S. Department of Defense
DNV	Det Norske Veritas
DOI	U.S. Department of the Interior
EIA	U.S. Energy Information Administration
GAO	U.S. General Accounting Office
HSE	Health and Safety Executive of the United Kingdom
IAEA	International Atomic Energy Agency
MMS	Minerals Management Service
NEI	Nuclear Energy Institute
NPC	National Petroleum Council
NTSB	National Transportation Safety Board
OECD	Organisation for Economic Cooperation and Development
Presidential Commission	National Commission on the BP *Deepwater Horizon* Oil Spill and Offshore Drilling
PSA	Petroleum Safety Authority of Norway
SINTEF	Stiftelsen for Industriell og Teknisk Forskning
USCG	U.S. Coast Guard
U.S. NRC	U.S. Nuclear Regulatory Commission

Aadnoy, B. S., I. Cooper, S. Z. Miska, R. F. Mitchell, and M. L. Payne. 2009. *Advanced Drilling and Well Technology.* Society of Petroleum Engineers, Richardson, Tex.

ABS. 2011. Setting Standards for Service. http://www.eagle.org/eagleExternalPortal WEB/. Most recently accessed Jan. 17, 2012.

Bea, R., I. Mitroff, D. Farber, H. Foster, and K. H. Roberts. 2009. A New Approach to Risk: The Implications of E3. *Risk Management,* Vol. 11, No. 1, pp. 30-43.

Bierly, P. E., III, and J. C. Spender. 1995. Culture and High Reliability Organizations: The Case of the Nuclear Submarine. *Journal of Management,* Vol. 21, No. 4, pp. 639-656.

BOEMRE. 2011. *Report Regarding the Causes of the April 20, 2010 Macondo Well Blowout.* http://www.boemre.gov/pdfs/maps/dwhfinal.pdf. Most recently accessed Jan. 17, 2012.

Bommer, P. 2008. *A Primer of Oilwell Drilling,* 7th ed. University of Texas at Austin.

Borthwick, D. 2010. *Report of the Montara Commission of Inquiry.* Commonwealth of Australia. http://www.ret.gov.au/Department/Documents/MIR/Montara-Report.p df. Most recently accessed Jan. 17, 2012.

Bourgoyne, A. T., M. E. Chenevert, K. K. Millheim, and F. S. Young, Jr. 1991. *Applied Drilling Engineering.* SPE Textbook Series, Vol. 2. Society of Petroleum Engineers, Richardson, Tex. http://store.spe.org/Applied-Drilling-Engineering-P10.as px. Most recently accessed Jan. 17, 2012.

BP. 2010. Deepwater Horizon *Accident Investigation Report.* http://www.bp.com/ liveassets/bp_internet/globalbp/globalbp_uk_english/gom_response/STAGING/local _assets/downloads_pdfs/Deepwater_Horizon_Accident_Investigation_Report.pd f. Most recently accessed Jan. 17, 2012.

CAIB. 2003. Organizational Causes: Evaluating Best Safety Practices. In *The CAIB Report—Volume 1,* pp. 182-184. http://caib.nasa.gov/news/report/pdf/vol1/full/caib_ report_volume1.pdf. Most recently accessed Jan. 17, 2012.

Carnes, W. E. 2011. *Highly Reliable Governance of Complex Socio-Technical Systems.* Deepwater Horizon Study Group Working Paper, Jan. http://ccrm.berkeley.edu/ pdfs_papers/DHSGWorkingPapersFeb16-2011/HighlyReliableGovernance-of-Co mplexSocio-TechnicalSystems-WEC_DHSG-Jan2011.pdf. Most recently accessed Jan. 17, 2012.

CCPS. 1992. *Plant Guidelines for Technical Management of Chemical Process Safety.* Center for Chemical Process Safety, American Institute of Chemical Engineers, New York.

CCPS. 2005. *Building Process Safety Culture: Tools to Enhance Process Safety Performance.* Center for Chemical Process Safety, American Institute of Chemical Engineers, New York. http://www.aiche.org/uploadedFiles/CCPS/Resources/Kno wledgeBase/Piper_Alpha.pdf. Most recently accessed Jan. 17, 2012.

Chief Counsel. 2011. *Macondo: The Gulf Oil Disaster.* Chief Counsel's Report, National Commission on the BP *Deepwater Horizon* Oil Spill and Offshore Drilling. http://www.oilspillcommission.gov/sites/default/files/documents/C21462-408_CCR_ for_web_0.pdf. Most recently accessed Jan. 17, 2012.

County of Santa Barbara. 2005. *Blowout at Union Oil's Platform A.* Planning and Development, Energy Division. http://www.countyofsb.org/energy/information/1969blo wout.asp. Most recently accessed Jan. 17, 2012.

Cronin, M. A., and L. R. Weingart. 2007. Representational Gaps, Information Processing, and Conflict in Functionally Diverse Teams. *Academy of Management Review,* Vol. 32, No. 2, pp. 761-773.

CSB. 2007. *Investigation Report: Refinery Explosion and Fire (15 Killed, 180 Injured) BP Texas City, Texas, March 23, 2005.* U.S. Chemical Safety and Hazardous Investigation Board Report No. 2005-04-I-TX. http://www.csb.gov/assets/docume nt/CSBFinalReportBP.pdf. Most recently accessed Jan. 17, 2012.

Cullen, W. 1990. *The Public Inquiry into the* Piper Alpha *Disaster.* HM Stationery Office, London.

DHSG. 2011. *Final Report on the Investigation of the Macondo Well Blowout.* http://ccrm.berkeley.edu/pdfs_papers/bea_pdfs/DHSGFinalReport-March2011-tag. pdf. Most recently accessed Jan. 17, 2012.

DNV. 2010. *Energy Report: Beaufort Sea Drilling Risk Study.* Project No. EP004855.

DNV. 2011a. *Forensic Examination of* Deepwater Horizon *Blowout Preventer, Vols. I and II (Appendices).* Final Report for U.S. Department of the Interior, Bureau of Ocean Energy Management, Regulation, and Enforcement, Washington, D.C. Report No. EP030842. http://www.boemre.gov/pdfs/maps/DNVReportVolI.pdf, http://www.usc g.mil/hq/cg5/cg545/dw/exhib/DNV%20BOP%20report%20-%20Vol%202%20%282% 29.pdf . Most recently accessed Jan. 17, 2012.

DNV. 2011b. *Addendum to Final Report: Forensic Examination of* Deepwater Horizon *Blowout Preventer.* Report No. EP030842. http://www.boemre.gov/pdfs/maps/Add endumFinal.pdf. Most recently accessed Jan. 17, 2012.

DoD. 2000. *Standard Practice for System Safety.* MIL-STD-882D. Feb. 10. http://www. everyspec.com/MIL-STD/MIL-STD+(0800+-+0899)/MIL_STD_882D_934/. Most recently accessed Jan. 17, 2012.

DOI. 2010a. *Increased Safety Measures for Energy Development on the Outer Continental Shelf for 30 CFR Part 250.* http://www.boemre.gov/eppd/PDF/EAInterimSafe tyRule.pdf. Most recently accessed Jan. 17, 2012.

DOI. 2010b. *Report to Secretary of Interior Ken Salazar, September 1, 2010.* Outer Continental Shelf Safety Oversight Board. http://www.noia.org/website/download .asp?id=40069. Most recently accessed Jan. 17, 2010.

EIA. 2008. The U.S. Petroleum and Natural Gas Industry. http://www.eia.doe.gov/emeu/ finance/usi&to/upstream/index.html#n9. Most recently accessed Jan. 17, 2012.

GAO. 2004. *Energy Markets: Effects of Mergers and Market Concentration in the U.S. Petroleum Industry.* GAO-04-96. http://www.gao.gov/new.items/d0496.pdf. Most recently accessed Jan. 17, 2012.

Gallander, F. 2010. Update to BOEM on JIP Study on Reliability of Subsea Blowout Preventers. Presented at BOEMRE Forum on Ocean Drilling; September 13, 2010; Lafayette, Louisiana; Panel II Presentation – 5. http://www.boemre.gov/forums/do cuments/Panel_II_Presentation_5_lafayette.pdf. Most recently accessed Feb. 2, 2012.

Gardner, C. 2010. Letter Report of Cement Test Results to the National Commission on the BP *Deepwater Horizon* Oil Spill and Offshore Drilling. Energy Technology Company, Houston, Tex., Oct. 26.

Hartley, R. S., J. N. Tolk, and D. J. Swaim. 2008. *High Reliability Operations: A Practical Guide to Avoid the System Accident.* Babcock and Wilcox Technical Services Pantex, U.S. Department of Energy.

Hickman, T. A. 1984. *Report One: The Loss of the Semisubmersible Drill Rig* Ocean Ranger *and Its Crew.* Royal Commission on the *Ocean Ranger* Marine Disaster, Ottawa, Canada.

Holand, P., and P. Skalle. 2001. *Deepwater Kicks and BOP Performance.* STF38 A01419. SINTEF, Trondheim, Norway. http://www.boemre.gov/tarprojects/383/

383%20AB%20Final%20report%20Deepwater%20Kicks%20and%20BOP%20Pe rformance.pdf. Most recently accessed Jan 17, 2012.

HSE. 2006. *Developing Process Safety Indicators: A Step-by-Step Guide for Chemical and Major Hazard Industries.* http://www.hse.gov.uk/pubns/books/hsg254.htm. Most recently accessed Jan. 17, 2012.

HSE. 2008. *A Guide to the Well Aspects of the Offshore Installations and Wells (Design and Construction, etc) Regulation 1996,* 2nd ed. http://www.hse.gov.uk/pubns/ priced/l84.pdf. Most recently accessed Jan. 17, 2012.

HSE. 2011. Offshore Research. http://www.hse.gov.uk/offshore/offshoreresearch.htm Most recently accessed Jan. 17, 2012.

IAEA. 1992. *The Chernobyl Accident: Updating of INSAG-1.* Safety Series No. 75-INSAG-7. Vienna, Austria. http://www-pub.iaea.org/MTCD/publications/PDF/Pub 913e_web.pdf. Most recently accessed Jan. 17, 2012.

Kallman, R. E., and E. D. Wheeler. 1984. *Coastal Crude in a Sea of Conflict .* Blake Printery and Publishing, San Luis Obispo, Calif., p. 63 (as cited in Presidential Commission 2011).

Leveson, N. G. 2011. *Engineering a Safer World: System Thinking Applied to Safety.* Massachusetts Institute of Technology Press, Cambridge.

Maclachlan, M. 2007. *An Introduction to Marine Drilling.* Oilfield Publications.

May, J. J., and H. Foss. 2000. Power Management System for the *Deepwater Horizon,* a Dynamically Positioned All Weather Semisubmersible. Presented at Marine Technology Society's Dynamic Positioning Conference, Oct. 17-18. http://www./ dynamic-positioning.com/dp2000/power_foss.pdf. Most recently accessed Jan. 17, 2012.

McNutt, M., R. Camilli, G. Guthrie, P. Hsieh, V. Labson, B. Lehr, D. Maclay, A. Ratzel, and M. Sogge. 2011. *Assessment of Flow Rate Estimates for the* Deepwater Horizon / *Macondo Well Oil Spill.* Flow Rate Technical Group Report to the National Incident Command, Interagency Solutions Group, March 10. http://www.doi.gov/deepwater horizon/loader.cfm?csModule=security/getfile&PageID=237763. Most recently accessed Jan. 17, 2012.

Meshkati, N. 1995. Human Factors in Process Plants and Facility Design. In *Cost-Effective Risk Assessment for Process Design* (R. D. Deshotels and R. Zimmerman, eds.), McGraw-Hill, New York, pp. 113-130.

Meshkati, N. 1999. Cultural Context of Nuclear Safety Culture: A Conceptual Model and Field Study. In *Nuclear Safety: A Human Factors Perspective* (J. Misumi, B. Wilpert, and R. Miller, eds.), Taylor and Francis, London, pp. 61-75.

MMS. 1999. *Investigation of Blowout and Fire Ship Shoal Block 354, OCS-G 15312 Well A-2, September 9, 1999.* Gulf of Mexico off the Louisiana Coast. MMS 2001-009. http://www.gomr.boemre.gov/homepg/offshore/safety/acc_repo/accin dex.html. Most recently accessed Jan. 13, 2012.

NEI. 2009. *Fostering a Strong Nuclear Safety Culture.* NEI 09-07. June. http://pbadup ws.nrc.gov/docs/ML0915/ML091590728.pdf. Most recently accessed Jan. 17, 2012.

NPC. 2006. Oil and Gas Technology Development. Topic Paper 26 in *Facing the Hard Truths About Energy.* http://downloadcenter.connectlive.com/events/npc071807/pdf-downloads/Study_Topic_Papers/26-TTG-OGTechDevelopment.pdf. Most recently accessed Jan. 17, 2012.

NTSB. 2010. *Collision of Two Washington Metropolitan Area Transit Authority Metrorail Trains near Fort Totten Station, Washington, D.C. June 22, 2009.* Railroad Accident Report NTSB/RAR-10/02, PB2010-916302, Notation 8133C. Adopted

July 27. http://www.ntsb.gov/doclib/reports/2010/RAR1002.pdf. Most recently accessed Jan. 17, 2012.

OECD. 2008. *Guidance on Developing Safety Performance Indicators Related to Chemical Accident Prevention, Preparedness, and Response*. Guidance for Industry. http://www.oecd.org/dataoecd/6/57/41269710.pdf. Most recently accessed Jan. 17, 2012.

Oedewald, P., E. Pietikäinen, and T. Reiman. 2011. *A Guidebook for Evaluating Organizations in the Nuclear Industry: An Example of Safety Culture Evaluation*. Report No. 2011:20, Swedish Radiation Safety Authority. http://www.stralsaker hetsmyndigheten.se/Global/Publikationer/Rapport/Sakerhet-vid-karnkraftverken/2011/SSM-Rapport-2011-20.pdf. Most recently accessed Jan. 17, 2012.

Paté-Cornell, M. E. 1990. Organizational Aspects of Engineering System Safety: The Case of Offshore Platforms. *Science*, Vol. 250, No. 4985, pp. 1210-1217.

Paté-Cornell, M. E. 1993. Learning from the *Piper Alpha* Accident: A Postmortem Analysis of Technical and Organizational Factors. *Risk Analysis*, Vol. 13, No. 2, pp. 215-232.

Presidential Commission. 2010. Causes of Blowout and Drilling Safety. Presentation at the5th Meeting on the BP Deepwater Horizon Oil Spill and Offshore Drilling, November 8-9, 2010, Washington, DC. http://www.oilspillcommission.gov/sites/de fault/files/meeting5/Master_Presentation_v2.pdf. Most recently accessed Jan. 17, 2012.

Presidential Commission. 2011. *Deep Water: The Gulf Oil Disaster and the Future of Offshore Drilling*. Report to the President. http://www.oilspillcommission.gov/sites/default/files/documents/DEEPWATER_ReporttothePresident_FINAL.pdf. Most recently accessed Jan. 17, 2012.

Presidential Commission Staff. 2011. *The History of Offshore Oil and Gas in the United States*. Staff Working Paper No. 22. http://www.oilspillcommission.gov/sites/de fault/files/documents/HistoryofDrillingStaffPaper22.pdf. Most recently accessed Jan. 17, 2012.

PSA. 2004. HSE and Culture. Petroleum Safety Authority Norway. http://www.ptil.no/get-file.php/z%20Konvertert/Products%20and%20services/Publications/Dokumenter/hes cultureny.pdf. Most recently accessed Jan. 17, 2012

PSA 2011a. Technical Report/Seminars/R&D. Petroleum Safety Authority Norway http://www.ptil.no/technical-reports-seminars-r-d/category162.html. Most recently accessed Jan. 6, 2012.

PSA. 2011b. Acknowledgment of Compliance (AOC). http://www.ptil.no/acknowledge ment-of-compliance-aoc/category159.html. Most recently accessed Jan. 17, 2012.

Rasmussen, J. 1997. Risk Management in a Dynamic Society: A Modeling Problem. *Safety Science*, Vol. 27, No. 2/3, pp. 183-213.

Rasmussen, J., and I. Svedung. 2000. *Proactive Risk Management in a Dynamic Society*. Swedish Rescue Services Agency, Karlstad. https://www.msb.se/RibData/Filer/pdf/16252.pdf. Most recently accessed Jan. 17, 2012.

Reason, J. 1997. *Managing the Risks of Organizational Accidents*. Ashgate, Burlington, Vt.

Republic of the Marshall Islands. 2011. Deepwater Horizon *Marine Casualty Investigation Report*. Office of the Maritime Administrator. http://www.register-iri.com/forms/upload/Republic_of_the_Marshall_Islands_DEEPWATER_HORIZON_M arine_Casualty_Investigation_Report-Low_Resolution.pdf. Most recently accessed Jan. 17, 2012.

Roberts, K. H., and D. M. Rousseau. 1989. Research in Nearly Failure-Free, High-Reliability Organizations: Having the Bubble. *IEEE Transactions on Engineering Management*, Vol. 36, No. 2, pp. 132-139.

Sabens, F. L., and V. L. Maki, Jr. 2002. Apparatus and Method for Estimating the Compressive Strength of Foam Cement. U.S. Patent No. U6,345,535B1. Date of patent: Feb. 12. http://www.google.com/patents?hl=en&lr=&vid=USPAT63455 35&id=_wIJAAAAEBAJ&oi=fnd&dq=Apparatus+and+Method+for+Estimating +the+Compressive+Strength+of+Foam+Cement%E2%80%9D&printsec=abstract t#v=onepage&q&f=false. Most recently accessed Jan. 17, 2012.

Smith, D. K. 1990. *Cementing*. SPE Monograph Vol. 4. Society of Petroleum Engineers, Richardson, Tex., pp. 82-122.

Transocean. 2008. *Well Control Complications/Emergency*. HQS-OPS-HS-01. http://de mocrats.energycommerce.house.gov/documents/20100512/TRO-Surface.BOP.Ope rations.From.Floating.Vessels.pdf. Most recently accessed Jan. 17, 2012.

Transocean. 2011a. *Macondo Well Incident*. Transocean Investigation Report Vols. I and II (Appendices). http://www.deepwater.com/fw/main/Public-Report-1076.html. Most recently accessed Jan. 17, 2012.

Transocean. 2011b. Response to Coast Guard Draft Report by Transocean Offshore Deepwater Drilling Inc. and Transocean Holdings LLC. http://www.deepwater.com/_file lib/FileCabinet/pdfs/Response_to_USCG_Draft_Report.pdf. Most recently accessed Jan. 17, 2012.

USCG. 2011. *Report of Investigation into the Circumstances Surrounding the Explosion, Fire, Sinking and Loss of Eleven Crew Members Aboard the Mobile Offshore Drilling Unit* Deepwater Horizon *in the Gulf of Mexico April 20-22, 2010, Vol. I*. https://www.hsdl.org/?view&did=6700. Most recently accessed Jan. 17, 2012.

U.S. NRC. 2009. *Internal Safety Culture Task Force: Final Report*. April.

U.S. NRC. 2011. *Safety Culture Policy Statement*. NUREG/BR-0500. June. http://pba dupws.nrc.gov/docs/ML1116/ML11165A021.pdf. Most recently accessed Jan. 17, 2012.

Weick, K. E., and K. M. Sutcliffe. 2001. *Managing the Unexpected*. Jossey-Bass, San Francisco, Calif.

West Engineering Services, Inc. 2002. *Mini Shear Study for U.S. Minerals Management Service*. Requisition No. 2-1011-1003. Dec. http://www.boemre.gov/tarprojects/ 455/Final%20Report.pdf. Most recently accessed Jan. 17, 2012.

West Engineering Services, Inc. 2004. *Shear Ram Capabilities Study for U.S. Minerals Management Service*. Requisition No. 3-4025-1001. Sept. http://www.boemre.gov/tarpro jects/463/(463)%20West%20Engineering%20Final%20Report.pdf. Most recently accessed Jan. 17, 2012.

Zoback, M. D. 2010. *Reservoir Geomechanics*. Cambridge University Press.

Appendix A

Statement of Task

At the request of DOI, a National Academy of Engineering/National Research Council (NAE/NRC) committee will be convened to examine the probable causes of the *Deepwater Horizon* explosion, fire, and oil spill in order to identify measures for preventing similar harm in the future. The NAE/NRC committee's review will focus on an assessment of technologies and practices and include the following tasks:

1. Examine the performance of the technologies and practices involved in the probable causes of the explosion, including the performance of the "blowout preventer" and related technology features, which ultimately led to an uncontrolled release of oil and gas into the Gulf of Mexico;

2. Identify and recommend available technology, industry best practices, best available standards, and other measures in the United States and around the world related to oil and gas deepwater exploratory drilling and well completion to avoid future occurrence of such events.

The NAE/NRC committee will issue two reports:

1. An interim letter report that addresses the probable causes of the *Deepwater Horizon* explosion, fire, and oil spill and identifies potential measures to avoid such events. This report will be issued no later than October 31, 2010, with the intent that the committee's preliminary findings and/or recommendations will be considered in the joint investigation by MMS (BOEM) and the Coast Guard, the Presidential Commission, and any other formal review or investigation of the *Deepwater Horizon* explosion, fire, and oil spill.

2. A final report that presents the committee's final analysis, including findings and/or recommendations, called for in tasks (1) and (2) above by June 1, 2011 (prepublication version of report), with relevant dissemination activities and a final published version to follow by December 30, 2011.

If at any time in the course of the NAE/NRC committee information-gathering activities information is acquired indicating a public health or safety risk, the NRC will notify DOI of the availability of such information.

The project is sponsored by the U.S. Department of the Interior.

Note: The prepublication version of the final report, initially due in June 2011, was completed in December 2011.

Appendix B

Public Agendas of the Committee on the Analysis of Causes of the *Deepwater Horizon* Explosion, Fire, and Oil Spill to Identify Measures to Prevent Similar Accidents in the Future

During the course of its study, the committee held 22 meetings. The agendas listed below indicate presenters and discussants who participated in public sessions.

MEETING ON AUGUST 12–13, 2010

Embassy Suites Washington, Convention Center
900 10th Street, Northwest
Washington, D.C. 20001

Thursday, August 12

Welcome, purpose of public session, and introduction of committee members
　　Donald Winter, Committee Chair

U.S. Department of the Interior
　　David Hayes, Deputy Secretary (via speakerphone)

Bureau of Ocean Energy Management, Regulation, and
Enforcement (BOEMRE)
　　Michael Bromwich, Director
　　David Dykes, Chief, Office of Safety Management, Field Operations,
　　　Gulf of Mexico Outer Continental Shelf (OCS) Region

John McCarroll, Manager, Lake Jackson District, Gulf of Mexico
OCS Region

Committee discussion with BOEMRE presenters

American Petroleum Institute (API)
Erik Milito, API Upstream Department
David Soffrin, API Standards Department
Andy Radford, API Upstream Department
Roland Goodman, API Standards Department

Committee discussion with API presenters

Open microphone for public comment

Friday, August 13

Welcome and purpose of public session
Donald Winter, Committee Chair

U.S. Coast Guard
Captain Eric Christensen, Chief, Vessel Activities

Committee discussion with Captain Christensen
Commander Jennifer Williams, Chief, Foreign and Offshore Vessel
Compliance Division
Lieutenant Commander Joseph Bowes, Program Manager, Offshore
Compliance Branch

Republic of the Marshall Islands, Office of the Maritime Administrator
Brian Poskaitis, Deputy Commissioner for Maritime Affairs

Committee discussion with Mr. Poskaitis
Captain Thomas Heinan, Deputy Commissioner for Maritime Affairs
Brian Bubar, Deputy Commissioner for Maritime Affairs

American Bureau of Shipping
Kenneth Richardson, Vice President of Energy Projects

Committee discussion with Mr. Richardson

MEETING ON SEPTEMBER 26, 2010

Keck Center of the National Academies
500 Fifth Street, Northwest
Washington, D.C. 20001

Welcome, purpose of public session, and introduction of committee members
        Donald Winter, Committee Chair

BP's Deepwater Horizon *Accident Investigation Report*
        Mark Bly, BP Group Head of Safety and Operations
        Tony Brock, Vice President, Health, Safety, Security, and the
                Environment (HSSE) and Engineering, BP Exploration (Alaska), Inc.
        Steve Robinson, Director and Vice President, BP Exploration
                (Alaska), Inc.
        Kent Corser, Drilling Engineering Manager, BP North America Gas
        Fereidoun Abbassian, Vice President, Drilling and Completions
                Technology
        Dave Wall, Vice President, HSSE and Integrity Management

Committee discussion with BP presenters

Halliburton presentation
        Thomas Roth, Vice President, Cementing
        John Gisclair, In-Site Support Coordinator, Energy Services Group

Committee discussion with Halliburton presenters

Marine Well Containment System
        C. R. (Charlie) Williams II, Chief Scientist, Well Engineering and
                Production Technology, Shell

Committee discussion with Mr. Williams

MEETING ON FEBRUARY 25, 2011

National Academies Keck Center
500 Fifth Street, Northwest
Washington, D.C. 20001

Presentation via teleconference on enacted and planned regulatory changes
made by BOEMRE since the *Deepwater Horizon* incident
        Tommy Beaudreau, Senior Advisor to the BOEMRE director

MEETING ON MARCH 11, 2011

JW Marriott Houston
5150 Westheimer
Houston, Texas 77056

Welcome, purpose of public sessions, and introduction of committee members
    Donald Winter, Committee Chair

Safety case example
    Charlie Williams, Chief Scientist, Well Engineering and Production
        Technology, Shell

Responses to committee's questions
    Bill Arnold; GM Health, Safety and Environment; Worldwide
        Exploration and Production, ConocoPhillips
    William Daugherty, Drilling Manager, ATP Oil and Gas Corporation
    Steve Kropla, Group Vice President, Operations/Accreditation,
        International Association of Drilling Contractors
    Charlie Williams, Chief Scientist, Well Engineering and Production
        Technology, Shell
    Richard Williams, President, Gulf of Mexico
    Aaron Swanson, Director, OCS Regulation, Baker Hughes

Responses to committee's questions
    Michael Denkl, HSE Manager, North America Offshore and Alaska,
        Schlumberger Limited
    Cory Loegering, Region Vice President, Deepwater Apache Corporation
    Jeremy Thigpen, President, Downhole and Pumping Group
    Renju Jose, Manager, Corporate Development, National Oilwell Varco

Appendix C

Findings, Observations, and Recommendations

This appendix presents a compilation of the findings, observations, and recommendations shown in the chapters of this report.[1] The sequence in which they are presented is according to the sequence of the chapters and is not intended to imply a sense of priority.

ABBREVIATIONS

ABS	American Bureau of Shipping
AMF	automatic mode function
BOP	blowout preventer
BSEE	Bureau of Safety and Environmental Enforcement
BSR	blind shear ram
CSR	casing shear ram
DoD	U.S. Department of Defense
DOI	U.S. Department of the Interior
DNV	Det Norske Veritas
EDS	emergency disconnect system
LMRP	lower marine riser package
MODU	mobile offshore drilling unit
MUX	multiplexer
OIM	offshore installation manager
ppg	pounds per gallon
ROV	remotely operated vehicle
SEMS	Safety and Environmental Management Systems
VBR	variable bore ram

---

[1]This compilation was not presented in the prepublication version of this report, which was issued in December 2011.

WELL DESIGN AND CONSTRUCTION

Findings

Summary Finding 2.1: The flow of hydrocarbons that led to the blowout of the Macondo well began when drilling mud was displaced by seawater during the temporary abandonment process.[2,3]

Summary Finding 2.2: The decision to proceed to displacement of the drilling mud by seawater was made despite a failure to demonstrate the integrity of the cement job even after multiple negative pressure tests. This was but one of a series of questionable decisions in the days preceding the blowout that had the effect of reducing the margins of safety and that evidenced a lack of safety-driven decision making.

Summary Finding 2.3: The reservoir formation, encompassing multiple zones of varying pore pressures and fracture gradients, posed significant challenges to isolation using casing and cement. The approach chosen for well completion failed to provide adequate margins of safety and led to multiple potential failure mechanisms.

Finding 2.4: The sequence of fluids used to cement the Macondo well included a low-density foamed slurry followed by a dense un-foamed tail slurry. The foam cement was designed to have a density of 14.5 ppg at the bottom of the well, but at the surface, where the foam was mixed, the density was extremely light at around 6 ppg. The tail slurry had a density of 16.7 ppg. Because of the extreme density imbalance, the heavy tail cement on top of the foamed cement would have been gravitationally unstable near the surface, and it probably fell into and perhaps through the foamed slurry. This would have had the unintended effect of leaving a tail slurry containing foamed cement in the shoe track at the bottom of the casing rather than leaving the heavy, un-foamed tail cement.

Finding 2.5: Foamed cement that may have been inadvertently left in the shoe track would likely not have developed the compressive strength of the un-foamed cement, nor would it have had the strength to resist crushing when the differential pressure across the cement was increased during the negative test.

---

[2]"Summary" indicates that a finding, observation, or recommendation is presented in the report summary.

[3]The first digit of a finding, observation, or recommendation refers to a chapter of this report in which it appears.

Finding 2.6: Evidence available before the blowout indicated that the flapper valves in the float collar probably failed to seal, but this evidence was not acted on at the time.

Finding 2.7: On the basis of photographic evidence, it appears that flow was up the inside of the casing, because the inside of the hanger showed signs of fluid erosion while the outside did not. However, not installing a lockdown sleeve left a potential for flow up the annulus.

Finding 2.8: Because of the choice of the long string of production casing, it was not possible to reciprocate or rotate the casing during the cementing operation. Casing movement tends to help remove any mud left in the path of the cement and force the cement into pathways that might otherwise be bypassed. The minimum circulation of mud was not achieved in this well, which would have been helpful in removing stagnant mud and debris from the annulus. Thus, the possibility of mud-filled channels or poor cement bonding existed.

Finding 2.9: No cement bond log was run to investigate the condition of the cement. The well design placed the float collar above the bottom of the deepest reservoir and would have prevented the log from investigating the lower sections of the well in which cement had been pumped.

Finding 2.10: Although data were being transmitted to shore, it appears that no one in authority (from BP onshore management or a regulatory agency) was required to examine test results and other critical data and render an opinion to the personnel on the rig before operations could continue.

Observations

Summary Observation 2.1: While the geologic conditions encountered in the Macondo well posed challenges to the drilling team, alternative completion techniques and operational processes were available that could have been used to prepare the well safely for temporary abandonment.

Observation 2.2: Had an attempt been made to bleed off the drill pipe pressure at the end of the negative test, the communication with the reservoir would likely have been discovered.

Observation 2.3: The results of a variety of static tests of foamed cement mixed at 14.5 ppg and exposed to atmospheric pressure call into question the stability of the foam, because settling of cement and breakout of nitrogen were observed in these tests. The tests were not performed at conditions that existed during pumping or at the bottom of the well and therefore cannot be considered as representative of the foam during displacement or at bottom hole conditions.

Observation 2.4: The pumping sequence of cement slurries and other fluids used for cementing the Macondo well subjected the volume of the lead cement slurry to contamination by the spacer or mud that was placed ahead of it. If it was heavily contaminated, the slurry would not have established a cement cap with the compressive strength of uncontaminated cement.

Observation 2.5: Had the path of the blowout been up the annulus, a liner top or the rupture discs could have failed and allowed flow to escape the well into a shallow formation. This would result in a downhole blowout that could breach at the seafloor under the correct conditions. Future well construction could avoid this possibility by running one of the deeper casing strings back to the wellhead where it can be sealed. For example, in this well the 13 $\frac{5}{8}$-inch liner could have been run back to the wellhead. This would protect the shallower liner tops and rupture discs from potential exposure to high pressure from flow up the annulus from a deeper reservoir.

Observation 2.6: The use of a production liner rather than the long string could have allowed for the use of a rotating liner hanger to improve the chances of good cement bonding; allowed for the use of a liner top packer to add a barrier to annular flow near the bottom of the well; allowed for the omission of the differential fill tube, which would remove a potential failure mechanism for the float collar; potentially made the negative test simpler to conduct and interpret; and configured the well to better control and repair a leak in the liner by leaving the well filled with drilling mud to a greater depth and by placing the drill pipe at a greater depth in the well during the test.

Recommendations

Summary Recommendation 2.1: Given the critical role that margins of safety play in maintaining well control, guidelines should be established to ensure that the design approach incorporates protection against the various credible risks associated with the drilling and completion processes.

Recommendation 2.2: During drilling, rig personnel should maintain a reasonable margin of safety between the equivalent circulating density and the density that will cause wellbore fracturing.

Summary Recommendation 2.3: All primary cemented barriers to flow should be tested to verify quality, quantity, and location of cement. The integrity of primary mechanical barriers (such as the float equipment, liner tops, and wellhead seals) should be verified by using the best available test procedures. All tests should have established procedures and predefined criteria for acceptable performance and should be subject to independent, near-real-time review by a competent authority.

Recommendation 2.4: The general well design should include the review of fitness of components for the intended use and be made a part of the well approval process.

Recommendation 2.5: Generally accepted good operational or best practices should be used in the construction of the well. Such practices would ensure that the most accurate well data are passed from the operator to the various contractors for use in simulations and design and that the results are considered by all parties before implementation.

BLOWOUT PREVENTER SYSTEM

Findings

Summary Finding 3.1: The loss of well control was not noted until more than 50 minutes after hydrocarbon flow from the formation started, and attempts to regain control by using the BOP were unsuccessful. The BSR failed to sever the drill pipe and seal the well properly, and the EDS failed to separate the lower marine riser and the *Deepwater Horizon* from the well.

Finding 3.2: The crew did not realize that the well was flowing until mud actually exited and was expelled out of the riser by the flow at 21:40. Early detection and control of flow from a reservoir are critical if an impending blowout is to be prevented by a BOP whose use against a full-flowing well is untested.

Finding 3.3: Once mud began to flow above the rig floor, the crew attempted to close the upper annular preventer of the BOP system, but it did not seal properly. The BOP system had been used in the month previously to strip 48 tool joints, and apparently it was untested for integrity afterwards. Annulars are often unable to seal properly after stripping. In addition, the flowing pressure inside the well may have been larger than the preset annular closing pressure could overcome. What tests of sealing against flow have been done on this design of annular are unknown.

Finding 3.4: The crew also closed the VBRs. The damaged pipe under the upper annular demonstrated its failure to seal, and the well was only sealed, resulting in the final pressure spike, when these VBRs were closed. The DNV investigation also found that these rams closed, and they could only be closed by command from the rig control panels and not by an ROV. At this point the flow from below the VBRs would have been closed off, but gas and oil had already flowed into the marine riser above the BOP system and continued to rise to the surface, where the gas exploded.

Finding 3.5: The internal BOP, which functions as a safety valve on the top of the drill pipe, was not closed (BP 2010, 25). Also, approximately 30 minutes after the explosion the traveling block was observed to fall and the rotary hose (used to conduct drilling fluid) could have been destroyed. The growing fire indicates that the drill pipe was broken in the initial explosion and the fall of the traveling block could have allowed even more flow to escape up the drill string. This was the likely path of hydrocarbon flow before the closure of the BSR.

Finding 3.6: Once the fire started on the rig, an attempt was made (after 7 minutes) to activate the EDS, which should have closed the BSR and disconnected the LMRP. This appears to have failed because the MUX communication cables were destroyed by the explosion or fire.

Finding 3.7: Once hydraulic and electrical connection with the rig was lost at the BOP, the AMF should have activated the BSR. It might have failed at this time because of a low battery charge in one control pod and a miswired solenoid valve in the other, but both these points are in dispute. However, no short-term reduction in hydrocarbon flow from the well was observed after the initial fire and explosion. Such a reduction would necessarily have resulted from the VBRs sealing the annulus in the BOP and the failed BSR shearing action effectively choking, at least for a brief period of time, virtually the entire cross section of the 5½-inch drill string. Viewed in total, the evidence appears more supportive of the autoshear activation of the BSR.

Finding 3.8: The BSR appears to have been activated after 07:40 on April 22, 2010, if not earlier, when the hydraulic plunger to the autoshear valve was cut by an ROV. However, regardless of when the BSR was activated, the well continued to flow out of control.

Finding 3.9: DNV hypothesized that the drill pipe below the annular preventer was being forced upward by the pressure of the flowing well, resulting in a 115,000-pound net compressive force on the drill pipe in the BOP sufficient to buckle the drill pipe until it came in contact with the inside of the BOP system (DNV 2011a, I, 174). However, the fluid mechanics inherent in this assumption are dubious. The 135,000 pounds of buoyed drill string weight above the BOP appears to be a more plausible source of the compression.

Finding 3.10: When it was activated, the BSR was unable to center the drill pipe in its blades and failed to cut the pipe completely. The blades of the ram were of the old straight and V combination, which has been shown to be inferior in its shearing performance to the double-V blade geometry (West Engineering Services 2004). Because the BSR blades did not fully span the BOP annular, a mashed segment of pipe was caught between the rams and prevented them from closing to the point where they could seal (DNV 2011b, 17).

Finding 3.11: After the rig lost power and drifted off station, the marine riser kept the vessel tethered to the BOP system.

Finding 3.12: Flow from the well then exited the partially severed drill pipe in the BSR and began to erode parts of the ram and BOP stack by fluid flow.

Finding 3.13: After the vessel sank at 10:22 on April 22, 2010, the marine riser with the drill pipe inside was bent at a number of places, including the connector to the BOP, and oil and gas began to flow into the ocean.

Finding 3.14: The effect of closing the CSR on April 29, 2010, was to provide a new flow path exiting the severed drill pipe below the CSR and passing the CSR rams that were not designed to seal. Severe fluid erosion occurred past the CSR, with deep cuts made in the surrounding steel of the BOP housing itself, endangering the integrity of the housing.

Finding 3.15: Unfortunately, even if the BSR had functioned after being activated by the EDS or the AMF, it would not likely have prevented the initial explosions, fire, and resulting loss of life, because hydrocarbons had already flowed into the marine riser above the BOP system. If the BOP system had been able to seal the well, the rig might not have sunk, and the resulting oil spill would likely have been minimized.

Summary Finding 3.16: The BOP system was neither designed nor tested for the dynamic conditions that most likely existed at the time that attempts were made to recapture well control. Furthermore, the design, test, operation, and maintenance of the BOP system were not consistent with a high-reliability, fail-safe device.

Finding 3.17: Regulations in effect before the incident required the periodic testing of the BOP system. However, they did not require testing under conditions that simulated the hydrostatic pressure at the depth of the BOP system or under the condition of pipe loading that actually occurred under dynamic flow, with the possible entrained formation rock, sand, and cement, and no such tests were run. Furthermore, because of the inadequate monitoring technology, the condition of the subsea control pods at the time of the blowout was unknown.

Finding 3.18: The committee's assessment of the available information on the capabilities and performance of the BOP system at the Macondo well points to a number of deficiencies (listed below) that are indicative of deficiencies in the design process. Past studies suggest that the shortcomings also may be present for BOP systems deployed for other deepwater drilling operations.

1. The committee could find no evidence that the BOP design criteria or performance envelope was ever fully integrated into an overall well control system perspective, nor that BOP design was consistent with the BOP's critical role in well control.

2. While individual subsystems of various BOP designs have been studied on an ad hoc basis over the years, the committee could find no evidence of a reliability assessment of the entire BOP system, which would have included functioning at depth under precisely the conditions of a dynamic well blowout. Furthermore, the committee could find no publicly available design criteria for BOP reliability.

3. The entire BOP system design is characterized by a previously identified lack of redundancy:
   • There is only one BSR.
   • One shuttle valve is used by both control pods.
   • Each MUX cable is incapable of monitoring the entire BOP system independently.

4. No design consideration appears to have been given to BSR performance on pipe in compression.

5. The BSR was not designed to shear all types and sizes of pipe that might be present in the BOP system.

6. The BSR probably did not have the capability of shearing or sealing any pipe in significant compression.

7. There was a lack of BOP status monitoring capabilities on the rig, including

- Battery condition,
- Condition of the solenoid valves,
- Flow velocity inside the BOP system,
- Ram position,
- Pipe and tool joint position inside the BOP system, and
- Detection of faults in the BOP system and cessation of drilling operations on that basis.

Finding 3.19: The failure of the AMF to activate might have been due to malfunctions in the control pods that could not be detected. In view of the state of the pipe in the well after the explosion, whether the BSR would have functioned properly is uncertain. This issue is moot if the rams could not perform their intended functions whenever they were activated.

Finding 3.20: The regulations did not require that the design of the equipment allow for real-time monitoring of critical features, such as the battery condition in the control pod, so that maintenance issues could be readily discovered. The current test protocol for the BSRs, for example, is designed for near-ideal surface conditions rather than the harsher conditions found on the ocean floor.

Finding 3.21: When a signal is sent from the drilling rig to the BOP (on the seafloor) to execute a command, the BOP sends a message back that the signal has been received. However, there are no transducers that detect the position or status of key components, and there are no devices to send a signal that any command has been executed (such as pressure or displacement sensors confirming that the hydraulics have been actuated, that rams have moved, or that pipe has been cut). Furthermore, there are no sensors to communicate flow or pressures in the BOP to the rig floor.

Observations

Observation 3.1: In the confusion of an emergency such as the one on the *Deepwater Horizon*, it is not surprising that a drill crew would not take the time to determine whether a tool joint was located in the plane of the BSR or whether tension was properly maintained in the drill pipe.

Observation 3.2: In terms of emergency procedures, such as an emergency disconnect or autoshear function of the BOP system on its own, there is no ability to manipulate the tool joint position or the level of tension or compression in the drill pipe. The BSR was not designed to work for the full range of conditions that could be realistically anticipated in an emergency.

Recommendations

Summary Recommendation 3.1: BOP systems should be redesigned to provide robust and reliable cutting, sealing, and separation capabilities for the drilling environment to which they are being applied and under all foreseeable operating conditions of the rig on which they are installed. Test and maintenance procedures should be established to ensure operability and reliability appropriate to their environment of application. Furthermore, advances in BOP technology should be evaluated from the perspective of overall system safety. Operator training for emergency BOP operation should be improved to the point that the full capabilities of a more reliable BOP can be competently and correctly employed when needed in the future.

Recommendation 3.2: The design capabilities of the BOP system should be improved so that the system can shear and seal all combinations of pipe under all possible conditions of load from the pipe and from the well flow, including entrained formation rock and cement, with or without human intervention. Such a system should be designed to go into the "well closed" position in the event of a system failure. This does not mean that the BOP must be capable of shearing every drill pipe at every point. It does mean that the BOP design should be such that for any drill string being used in a particular well, there will always be a shearable section of the drill pipe in front of some BSR in the BOP.

Recommendation 3.3: The performance of the design capabilities described in the preceding recommendation should be demonstrated and independently certified on a regular basis by test or other means.

Recommendation 3.4: The instrumentation on the BOP system should be improved so that the functionality and condition of the BOP can be monitored continuously.

Summary Recommendation 3.5: Instrumentation and expert system decision aids should be used to provide timely warning of loss of well control to drillers on the rig (and ideally to onshore drilling monitors as well). If the warning is inhibited or not addressed in an appropriate time interval, autonomous operation of the BSRs, EDS, general alarm, and other safety systems on the rig should occur.[4]

Recommendation 3.6: An unambiguous procedure, supported with proper instrumentation and automation, should be created for use as part of the

---

[4]This recommendation is repeated as Summary Recommendation 4.1.

BOP system. The operational status of the system, including battery charge and pressures, should be continuously monitored from the surface.

Recommendation 3.7: A BOP system with a critical component that is not operating properly, or one that loses redundancy in a critical component, should cause drilling operations to cease. Drilling should not resume until the BOP's emergency operation capability is fully cured.

Recommendation 3.8: A reliable and effective EDS is needed to complete the three-part objective of cutting, sealing, and separating as a true "dead man" operation when communication with the rig is lost. The operation should not depend on manual intervention from the rig, as was the case with the *Deepwater Horizon*. The components used to implement this recommendation should be monitored or tested as necessary to ensure their operation when needed.

If the consequence of losing communication and status monitoring of the BOP system is an automatic severing of the drill pipe and disconnection from the well, the quality and reliability of this communication link will improve dramatically.

Recommendation 3.9: BOP systems should be designed to be testable without concern for compromising the integrity of the system for future use.

MOBILE OFFSHORE DRILLING UNITS

Findings

Summary Finding 4.1: Once well control was lost, the large quantities of gaseous hydrocarbons released onto the *Deepwater Horizon*, exacerbated by low wind velocity and questionable venting selection, made ignition all but inevitable.

Finding 4.1a: Uncontrolled flow of hydrocarbons through the derrick resulted in a huge cloud of combustible atmosphere surrounding the rig.

Finding 4.1b: The rig was not designed to prevent explosion or fire once it was surrounded by the extent of combustible atmosphere facing the *Deepwater Horizon*.

Finding 4.1c: Hydrocarbon flow was not redirected overboard. Overboard discharge of the blowout might have delayed the explosion and fire aboard the rig.

Finding 4.1d: Explosions and subsequent fire are suspected to have resulted from ignition of the surrounding combustible cloud; the source of the ignition cannot be definitively determined.

Finding 4.2: Loss of power led to a broad range of effects including loss of firefighting ability, position-keeping ability, and overall situational control.

Finding 4.2a: The rig's dynamic positioning system operated as designed until the loss of power disabled the rig's ability to maintain station or reposition under control.

Finding 4.2b: Backup system designs did not ensure reliable power.

Finding 4.2c: The standby generator did not automatically start and could not be started in manual mode, indicating deficient reliability in the backup system needed to restore main generator power.

Finding 4.2d: Poor performance by the standby diesel generator may indicate that insufficient environmental testing was specified for this critical, last-resort power system to demonstrate robust capability or any local indication of generator starting availability.

Finding 4.3: Alarm and indication systems, procedures, and training were insufficient to ensure timely and effective actions to prevent the explosions or respond to save the rig.

Finding 4.3a: The rig design did not employ automatic methods to react to indications of a massive blowout, leaving reactions entirely in the hands of the surviving crew.

Finding 4.3b: The crew was ill-prepared for the scale of this disaster.

Finding 4.3c: Watch officers were not trained to respond to the conditions faced in this incident.

Finding 4.3d: Emergency procedures did not equip the watch standers with immediate actions to minimize damage and loss of life.

Finding 4.3e: The training routine did not include any full rig drills designed to develop and maintain crew proficiency in reacting to major incidents.

Finding 4.3f: Training of key personnel did not include realistic blowout scenarios or the handling of multiple concurrent failures.

Finding 4.3g: Crew members lacked cross-rate training to understand rig total systems and components. As a result, many of the crew were inadequately prepared to react to the incident.

Finding 4.4: Confusion existed about decision authority and command. Uncertainty as to whether the rig was under way or moored to the well-head contributed to the confusion on the bridge and may have impaired timely disconnect.

Finding 4.5: The U.S. Coast Guard's requirement for the number and placement of lifeboats was shown to be prudent and resulted in sufficient lifeboat capacity for effective rig abandonment. The Coast Guard's investigation report (USCG 2011) notes a lack of heat shielding to protect escape paths and life-saving equipment.

Finding 4.6: The above findings indicate that the lack of fail-safe design and testing, training, and operating practices aboard the rig contributed to loss of the rig and loss of life. The chain of events that began downhole could have been interrupted at many points, such as at the wellhead by the BOP or aboard the rig, where the flow might have been directed overboard or where the rig itself might have been disconnected from the well and repositioned. Had the rig been able to disconnect, the primary fuel load for the fire would have been eliminated.

Observations

Observation 4.1: The actions of some crew members in requiring due consideration of additional survivors before launching lifeboats, despite the fearsome fires engulfing the rig, are commendable and were important in the highly successful evacuation.

Observation 4.2: The attempts to start the standby diesel generator and restore power for damage control were acts of bravery.

Observation 4.3: Conditions of explosion, fire, loss of lighting, toxic gas, and eventual flooding and sinking could have resulted in many more injuries or deaths if not for the execution of the rig's evacuation.

Observation 4.4: ABS rules require that propulsion control systems for MODUs shall "in general" comply with the Steel Vessel Rules. This requirement may give rise to ambiguity concerning primary control and monitoring systems on MODUs.

Recommendations

Summary Recommendation 4.1: Instrumentation and expert system decision aids should be used to provide timely warning of loss of well control to drillers on the rig (and ideally to onshore drilling monitors as well). If the warning is inhibited or not addressed in an appropriate time interval, autonomous operation of the BSRs, EDS, general alarm, and other safety systems on the rig should occur.[5]

Recommendation 4.2: Rigs should be designed so that their instrumentation, expert system decision aids, and safety systems are robust and highly reliable under all foreseeable normal and extreme operating conditions. The design should account for hazards that may result from drilling operations and attachment to an uncontrolled well. The aggregate effects of cascading casualties and failures should be considered to avoid the coupling of failure modes to the maximum reasonable extent.

Recommendation 4.3: Industry and regulators should develop fail-safe design requirements for the combined systems of rig, riser, BOP, drilling equipment, and well to ensure that (*a*) blowouts are prevented and (*b*) if a blowout should occur the hydrocarbon flow will be quickly isolated and the rig can disconnect and reposition. The criteria for these requirements should be maximum reasonable assurance of (*a*) and (*b*) and successful crew evacuation under both scenarios.

Recommendation 4.4: Industry and regulators should implement a method of design review for systemic risks for future well design that uses a framework with attributes similar to those of the Department of Defense *Standard Practice for System Safety* (DoD 2000), which articulates standard practices for system safety for the U.S. military, to address the complex and integrated "system of systems" challenges faced in safely operating deepwater drilling rigs. The method should take into consideration the coupled effects of well design and rig design.

Recommendation 4.5: Industry should institute design improvements in systems, technology, training, and qualification to ensure that crew members are best prepared to cope with serious casualties.

Recommendation 4.6: ABS should eliminate any ambiguity in its rules requiring that propulsion control systems for MODUs shall "in general" comply with the Steel Vessel Rules. All of the primary control and monitoring systems and critical backup systems on these MODUs should be designed and tested to the highest standards in the industry.

---

[5]This recommendation is repeated as Summary Recommendation 3.5.

Recommendation 4.7: Industry should develop and implement passive or automatic methods to redirect hydrocarbon flow overboard. Ideally, the methods would include some artificial intelligence capability to evaluate the magnitude of the flow and prevailing wind.

Recommendation 4.8: Recovery of main electrical power is a vital capability for MODUs. Industry should ensure that standby generator systems will be reliable and robust for automatic starting. Moreover, standby generator location, controls, and power lines should be positioned to minimize the likelihood of damage from fire or explosions in the main engine room or from other casualties affecting the primary electric power system.

Recommendation 4.9: Data logger systems should be designed for handling the bandwidth of sensor data that may arise under the most stressing casualty conditions. The systems should be able to transmit in real time to shore so that accurate records are potentially available for determination of root cause in subsequent investigation.

Recommendation 4.10: Inhibition of alarms should be allowed only when approved by a senior officer in the vessel. Regulators should require that the master, OIM, and chief engineer review periodically the status of alarms and indications and take action to resolve conditions of complacent behavior. This should be a standard item of regulatory and class inspections.

Recommendation 4.11: Drilling rig contractors should review designs to ensure adequate redundancy in alarms and indicators in key areas of the rig.

Recommendation 4.12: Drilling rig contractors should require realistic and effective training in operations and emergency situations for key personnel before assignment to any rig. Industry should also require that personnel aboard the rig achieve and maintain a high degree of expertise in their assigned watch station, including formal qualification and periodic reexamination.

Recommendation 4.13: Realistic simulators should be used to expose key operators to conditions of stress that are expected in major conflagrations, including heat and loss of visibility.

Recommendation 4.14: Realistic major drill scenarios with independent oversight should be part of the normal routine at sea.

Recommendation 4.15: Regulators should require that all permanent crew on a rig achieve a basic level of qualification in damage control and escape systems to ensure that all hands are able to contribute to resolving a major casualty.

Recommendation 4.16: Regulators should increase the qualification requirements of the OIM to reflect a level of experience commensurate with the consequences of potential failure in his or her decision making.

Recommendation 4.17: Definition of command at sea should be absolutely unambiguous and should not change during emergencies.

Recommendation 4.18: Regulators should establish the unity of command and clearly articulate the hierarchy of roles and responsibilities of company man, master, and OIM.

Recommendation 4.19: Operating companies and drilling contractors should institute a certification authority, accountable to the head of the company, to act as the senior corporate official responsible and accountable for meeting the conditions set out in a safety management system. This appointment should provide a powerful voice for safe execution of operations and surety in dealing with emergencies: the official should have the authority and responsibility to stop work if necessary.

Recommendation 4.20: Industry and regulators should consider relevant aspects of programs for system safety certification that were established for other safety-critical large-scale activities, such as the U.S. Navy's Submarine Safety Program, as guidance in developing a response to the *Deepwater Horizon* incident.

Recommendation 4.21: Industry and regulators should develop and implement a certification to ensure that design requirements, material condition, maintenance, modernization, operating and emergency instructions, manning, and training are all effective in meeting the requirements of Recommendation 4.3 throughout the rig's service life.

Recommendation 4.22: Regulators should require that the rig, the entire system, and the crew be examined annually by an experienced and objective outside team to achieve and maintain certification in operational drilling safeguards. The consequence of unsatisfactory findings should be suspension of the crew's operation except under special supervisory conditions.

INDUSTRY MANAGEMENT OF OFFSHORE DRILLING

Finding

Summary Finding 5.1: The actions, policies, and procedures of the corporations involved did not provide an effective system safety approach commensurate with the risks of the Macondo well. The lack of a strong safety culture resulting from a deficient overall systems approach to safety is evident in the multiple flawed decisions that led to the blowout. Industrial management involved with the Macondo well–*Deepwater Horizon* disaster failed to appreciate or plan for the safety challenges presented by the Macondo well.

Observations

Summary Observation 5.1: The ability of the oil and gas industry to perform and maintain an integrated assessment of the margins of safety for a complex well like Macondo is impacted by the complex structure of the offshore oil and gas industry and the divisions of technical expertise among the many contractors engaged in the drilling effort.

Observation 5.2: Processes within the oil and gas industry to assess adequately the integrated risks associated with drilling a deepwater well, such as Macondo, are currently lacking.

Observation 5.3: As offshore drilling extends into deeper water, its complexity increases. However, in-house technical capabilities within many operating companies for well drilling operations have diminished in favor of reliance on multiple contractors. This, in turn, diminishes the capacity of operations companies (the "operator") to assess and integrate the multiplicity of factors potentially affecting the safety of the well.

Observation 5.4: The operating leaseholder company is the only entity involved in offshore drilling that is positioned to manage the overall system safety of well drilling and rig operations.

Summary Observation 5.5: The extent of industry training of key personnel and decision makers has been inconsistent with the complexities and risks of deepwater drilling.

Observation 5.6: There are too few standardized requirements across companies for education, training, and certification of personnel involved in deepwater drilling.

Summary Observation 5.7: Overall, the companies involved have not made effective use of real-time data analysis, information on precursor incidents or near misses, or lessons learned in the Gulf of Mexico and worldwide to adjust practices and standards appropriately.

Summary Observation 5.8: Industry's R&D efforts have been focused disproportionately on exploration, drilling, and production technologies as opposed to safety.

Recommendations

Summary Recommendation 5.1: Operating companies should have ultimate responsibility and accountability for well integrity, because only they are in a position to have visibility into all its aspects. Operating companies should be held responsible and accountable for well design, well construction, and the suitability of the rig and associated safety equipment. Notwithstanding the above, the drilling contractor should be held responsible and accountable for the operation and safety of the offshore equipment.[6]

Recommendation 5.1a: Coordination of multiple contractors should be reinforced to maintain a common focus on overall safety.

Recommendation 5.1b: Operating companies should develop and maintain the proper oversight of contractor work.

Summary Recommendation 5.2: Industry should greatly expand R&D efforts focused on improving the overall safety of offshore drilling in the areas of design, testing, modeling, risk assessment, safety culture, and systems integration. Such efforts should encompass well design, drilling and marine equipment, human factors, and management systems. These endeavors should be conducted to benefit the efforts of industry and government to instill a culture of safety.

Summary Recommendation 5.3: Industry should undertake efforts to expand significantly the formal education and training of industry personnel engaged in offshore drilling to support proper implementation of system safety.

Recommendation 5.3a: Education of rig personnel early in their careers can be provided through a system similar to community or technical colleges.

---

[6]This recommendation is also presented as Summary Recommendation 6.20.

Recommendation 5.3b: In addition to rig personnel, onshore personnel involved in overseeing or supporting rig-based operations should have sufficient understanding of the fundamental processes and risks involved.

Recommendation 5.3c: A research process is needed for establishing standardized requirements for education, training, and certification of everyone working on an offshore drilling rig. Additional standardized requirements should be established for education, training, and certification of key drilling-related personnel working offshore and onshore.

Summary Recommendation 5.4: Industry and regulators should improve corporate and industrywide systems for reporting safety-related incidents. Reporting should be facilitated by enabling anonymous or "safety privileged" inputs. Corporations should investigate all such reports and disseminate their lessons-learned findings in a timely manner to all their operating and decision-making personnel and to the industry as a whole. A comprehensive lessons-learned repository should be maintained for industrywide use. This information can be used for training in accident prevention and continually improving standards.[7]

Summary Recommendation 5.5: Industry should foster an effective safety culture through consistent training, adherence to principles of human factors, system safety, and continued measurement through leading indicators.

Recommendation 5.5a: The committee endorses the concept of a "center for offshore safety" to train, monitor the work experience of, and certify (license) personnel. Leadership of the center should involve persons affiliated with one or more neutral organizations that are outside of the petroleum industry.

Recommendation 5.5b: Effective response to a crisis situation requires teamwork to share information and perform actions. Training should involve on-site team exercises to develop competent decision making, coordination, and communication. Emergency team drills should involve full participation, as would be required in actual emergency situations, including a well blowout. Companies should approach team training as a means of instilling overall safety as a high priority.

Recommendation 5.5c: Use of training simulators similar to those applied in the aerospace industry and the military should be considered.

---

[7]This recommendation is also presented as Summary Recommendation 6.14.

Approaches using simulators should include team training for coordination of activities in crisis situations.

Summary Recommendation 5.6: Efforts to reduce the probability of future blowouts should be complemented by capabilities of mitigating the consequences of a loss of well control. Industry should ensure timely access to demonstrated well-capping and containment capabilities.

REGULATORY REFORM

Observations

Summary Observation 6.1: The regulatory regime was ineffective in addressing the risks of the Macondo well. The actions of the regulators did not display an awareness of the risks or the very narrow margins of safety.

Summary Observation 6.2: The extent of training of key personnel and decision makers in regulatory agencies has been inconsistent with the complexities and risks of deepwater drilling.

Summary Observation 6.3: Overall, the regulatory community has not made effective use of real-time data analysis, information on precursor incidents or near misses, or lessons learned in the Gulf of Mexico and worldwide to adjust practices and standards appropriately.

Recommendations

Summary Recommendation 6.1: The United States should fully implement a hybrid regulatory system that incorporates a limited number of prescriptive elements into a proactive, goal-oriented risk management system for health, safety, and the environment.

Recommendation 6.2: BSEE should continue to work closely with private industry and other agencies in adopting and developing comprehensive goals and standards to govern the many processes and systems involved in offshore drilling.

Recommendation 6.3: BSEE should make effective use of existing industry standards, well-established international standards, and best practice guidelines used by other countries, but it should recognize that standards need to be updated and revised continually.

Recommendation 6.4: As the SEMS program moves forward in the United States, BSEE should incorporate the steps already taken by private industry (and industry associations and consortia) to improve offshore drilling safety after the *Deepwater Horizon* accident.

Recommendation 6.5: Quantitative risk analysis should be an essential part of goal-oriented risk management systems.

Summary Recommendation 6.6: BSEE and other regulators should identify and enforce safety-critical points during well construction and abandonment that warrant explicit regulatory review and approval before operations can proceed.

Recommendation 6.7: To augment SEMS, BSEE should work closely with private industry to develop a list of safety-critical points during well construction and abandonment that will require explicit regulatory review and approval before operations can proceed.

Recommendation 6.8: As part of a hybrid risk management system, BSEE should establish safe operating limits, which, when exceeded, would require regulatory approval for operations to proceed.

Recommendation 6.9: BSEE should incorporate requirements for approval and certification of key steps during well construction into codes and standards.

Recommendation 6.10: BSEE should review existing codes and standards to determine which should be improved regarding requirements for (*a*) use of state-of-the-art technologies, especially in areas related to well construction, cementing, BOP functionality, and alarm and evacuation systems, among others, and (*b*) approval and certification incumbent to management of changes in original plans for well construction.

Recommendation 6.11: The manner in which the above-mentioned codes and standards will be enforced should be specified by BSEE in the well plan submitted by operating companies for approval.

Recommendation 6.12: BSEE should adopt a system of precertification of operators, contractors, and service companies before granting a drilling permit for especially challenging projects.

Recommendation 6.13: BSEE should consider the use of independent well examiners to help in reviewing well plans and in regularly monitoring ongoing activities during drilling, completion, and abandonment.

Summary Recommendation 6.14: Industry, BSEE, and other regulators should improve corporate and industrywide systems for reporting safety-related incidents. Reporting should be facilitated by enabling anonymous or "safety privileged" inputs. Corporations should investigate all such reports and disseminate their lessons-learned findings in a timely manner to all their operating and decision-making personnel and to the industry as a whole. A comprehensive lessons-learned repository should be maintained for industrywide use. This information can be used for training in accident prevention and continually improving standards.[8]

Summary Recommendation 6.15: A single U.S. government agency should be designated with responsibility for ensuring an integrated approach for system safety for all offshore drilling activities.

Recommendation 6.16: As a first step, DOI should work with other departments and agencies with jurisdiction over some aspect of offshore drilling activities to simplify and streamline the regulatory process for drilling on the U.S. outer continental shelf.

Recommendation 6.17: BSEE should work with other federal agencies to delegate supporting regulatory responsibilities and accountabilities for ensuring system safety, integrating all aspects of system safety for the parts of offshore drilling operations in which a particular agency is involved. BSEE should strive to involve the domain expertise and core competencies of the other relevant agencies. BSEE should have purview over integrating regulation, inspection, and monitoring enforcement for all aspects of system safety for offshore drilling operations.

Recommendation 6.18: BSEE should work with other federal agencies to develop efficient and effective mechanisms for investigating future accidents and incidents.

Recommendation 6.19: DOI should require BSEE to provide the Secretary of the Interior with a net assessment of the risks of future drilling activities so that such risks can be factored into decisions with regard to new leases. Focusing on system safety, the assessment should be a formal probabilistic risk analysis that evaluates risks associated with all operations having the potential for significant harm to individuals, environmental damage, or economic loss. The operations addressed by the assessment should include drilling and well construction, temporary well abandonment, oil and gas production, and eventual well abandonment.

Summary Recommendation 6.20: Operating companies should have ultimate responsibility and accountability for well integrity, because only they are in a position to have visibility into all aspects. Operating companies

---

[8]This recommendation is also presented as Summary Recommendation 5.4.

should be held responsible and accountable for well design, well construction, and the suitability of the rig and associated safety equipment. Notwithstanding the above, the drilling contractor should be held responsible and accountable for the operation and safety of the offshore equipment.[9]

Recommendation 6.21: In carrying out its regulatory responsibilities, BSEE should view operating companies as taking full responsibility for the safety of offshore equipment and its use.

Recommendation 6.22: While the operating company is recognized to have the principal responsibility for compliance with rules and regulations governing offshore operations, BSEE should require the partner companies (as co-lease holders) to have a "see to" responsibility to ensure that the operator conducts activities in such a manner that risk is as low as reasonably practicable.

Summary Recommendation 6.23: BSEE and other regulators should undertake efforts to expand significantly the formal education and training of regulatory personnel engaged in offshore drilling roles to support proper implementation of system safety.

Recommendation 6.24: BSEE should exert every effort to recruit, develop, and retain experienced and capable technical experts with critical domain competencies.

Summary Recommendation 6.25: BSEE and other regulators should foster an effective safety culture through consistent training, adherence to principles of human factors, system safety, and continued measurement through leading indicators.

Recommendation 6.26: As a regulator, BSEE should enhance its internal safety culture to provide a positive example to the drilling industry through its own actions and the priorities it establishes.

REFERENCES

BP. 2010. Deepwater Horizon *Accident Investigation Report*, http://www.bp.com/liveassets/bp_internet/globalbp/globalbp_uk_english/gom_response/STAGING/local_assets/downloads_pdfs/Deepwater_Horizon_Accident_Investigation_Report.pdf. Most recently accessed Jan. 17, 2012.

DNV. 2011a. *Forensic Examination of Deepwater Horizon Blowout Preventer, Vols. 1 and 2 (Appendices).* Final Report for U. S. Department of the Interior, Bureau of Ocean Energy Management, Regulation, and Enforcement, Washington, D.C. Re-

---

[9]This recommendation is also presented as Summary Recommendation 5.1.

port No. EP030842. http://www.boemre.gov/pdfs/maps/DNVReportVolI.pdf, http://www.uscg.mil/hq/cg5/cg545/dw/exhib/DNV%20BOP%20report%20-%20Vol%202%20%282%29.pdf . Most recently accessed Jan. 17, 2012.

DNV. 2011b. *Addendum to Final Report: Forensic Examination of* Deepwater Horizon *Blowout Preventer.* Report No. EP030842. http://www.boemre.gov/pdfs/maps/AddendumFinal.pdf. Most recently accessed Jan. 17, 2012.

DoD. 2000. *Standard Practice for System Safety.* MIL-STD-882D. Feb. 10. http://www.everyspec.com/MIL-STD/MIL-STD+(0800+-+0899)/MIL_STD_882D_934/. Most recently accessed Jan. 17, 2012.

USCG. 2011. *Report of Investigation into the Circumstances Surrounding the Explosion, Fire, Sinking and Loss of Eleven Crew Members aboard the Mobile Offshore Drilling Unit* Deepwater Horizon *in the Gulf of Mexico April 20–22, 2010, Vol. I.* https://www.hsdl.org/?view&did=6700. Most recently accessed Jan. 17, 2012.

West Engineering Services, Inc. 2004. *Shear Ram Capabilities Study for U.S. Minerals Management Service.* Requisition No. 3-4025-1001. Sept. http://www.boemre.gov/tarprojects/463/(463)%20West%20Engineering%20Final%20Report.pdf. Most recently accessed Jan. 17, 2012.

Appendix D

Calculating the Differential Pressure at the Start of the Negative Test and the Quality of Foam Cement

See the well diagram in Figure D-1.

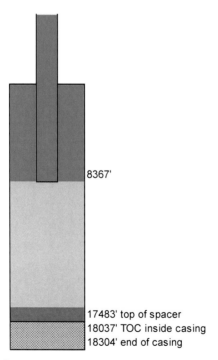

FIGURE D-1 Well diagram.

1. Pressure differential at the start of the negative test:

$\Delta p = p_o - p_i$

where

    Δp = pressure differential [pounds per square inch (psi)];
    p_o = pressure outside the casing at the bottom (psi), assumed equal to reservoir pressure of 11,892 psi, which is a pore pressure of 12.57 pounds per gallon (ppg) at the bottom of the reservoir at 18,212 feet (true vertical depth); and
    p_i = pressure on the inside above the cement (psi).

$$\Delta p = 11,892 - \frac{0.433}{8.33}[8,367(8.66) + 9,116(14.17) + 554(14.3)] = 999 \text{ psi}$$

Here the differential is into the casing. The cement is treated as a solid that does not transmit hydrostatic pressure but that must be strong enough to withstand the pressure differential across it. The top of the cement inside the casing is based on the assumption that 2.8 barrels of foam cement flowed back into the casing when the pressure was bled off at the end of the cement job.

    2.   Foam quality calculations:

Foam cement: The purpose in this case is to reduce the bottom hole (in situ) density of the slurry from 16.74 ppg to 14.5 ppg. The bottom hole pressure is the hydrostatic pressure of 14 ppg mud or 13,321 pounds per square inch gauge (psig) at 18,304 feet. The static bottom hole temperature is 245°F.

$\rho_s = 16.74 f_c + \rho_N f_N$

where

    $1 = f_c + f_N$,
    ρ_s = slurry density (lb$_m$/gal),
    ρ_N = nitrogen density (lb$_m$/gal),
    f_c = weight fraction of cement base slurry, and
    f_N = weight fraction of nitrogen.

$$\rho_N = 2.7\frac{\gamma_N p}{zT} = 2.7(0.9672)\frac{13,335.7}{1.71(705)} = 28.9\frac{\text{lb}_m}{\text{ft}^3}\frac{\text{ft}^3}{7.48 \text{ gal}} = 3.86\frac{\text{lb}_m}{\text{gal}}$$

$f_N = (14.5 - 16.74)/(-16.74 + 3.86) = 0.174$

$f_c = 0.826$

where

γ_N = specific gravity of nitrogen (compared with air),
p = pressure (pounds per square inch absolute),
z = gas deviation factor (dimensionless), and
T = temperature (degrees Rankine = 460 + degrees Fahrenheit).

So, for every in situ gallon of slurry there will be 0.174 gallon of nitrogen mixed with 0.826 gallon of base 16.74-ppg cement slurry. Thus, the in situ foam quality is 17.4 percent. Note that the Chevron tests used a 13 percent quality foam, which corresponds to the weight fraction of nitrogen necessary to create a 14.5 ppg density foam at atmospheric conditions. Therefore, more nitrogen is required to create the same density foam at the much higher pressure and temperature of the bottom of the Macondo well.

At the mixer at the surface, the slurry is blended and pumped at about 600 psig. The volume of nitrogen introduced to 0.826 gallons of base cement is the in situ volume increased through the real gas law.

$$V_{600} = 0.174 \frac{0.979}{1.71} \frac{520}{614.7} \frac{13,335.7}{705} = 1.6 \text{ gallons}$$

This is added to 0.826 gallon of base cement. Thus, for every 1 gallon of base cement, 1.94 gallons of N_2 at 600 psig is required. This is a 66 percent quality foam.

The density of the foam slurry at the mixer will be as follows:

$$\rho_N = 2.7(0.9672) \frac{614.7}{0.979(520)} = 3.15 \frac{\text{lb}_m}{\text{ft}^3} = 0.42 \frac{\text{lb}_m}{\text{gal}}$$

$$\rho_s = 16.74(0.34) + 0.42(0.66) = 5.97 \frac{\text{lb}_m}{\text{gal}}$$

The previous equations and results can be combined to obtain an equation for the density of the slurry at any depth with a corresponding pressure, temperature, and gas deviation factor.

$$\rho_s = 16.74(1 - f_N) + \rho_N f_N$$

$$\rho_N = \frac{2.7(0.9672)}{7.48} \frac{p}{Tz} = 0.349 \frac{p}{Tz}$$

$$f_N = \frac{V_N}{V_N + 0.826}$$

$$V_N = 0.174 \frac{Tz}{p} \frac{13,335.7}{1.71(705)} = 1.925 \frac{Tz}{p}$$

$$\rho_s = 16.74 \left(1 - \frac{1.925 \dfrac{Tz}{p}}{1.925 \dfrac{Tz}{p} + 0.826} \right) + 0.349 \frac{p}{Tz} \frac{1.925 \dfrac{Tz}{p}}{1.925 \dfrac{Tz}{p} + 0.826}$$

$$\rho_s \left(1.925 \frac{Tz}{p} + 0.826 \right) = 16.74 \left(1.925 \frac{Tz}{p} + 0.826 - 1.925 \frac{Tz}{p} \right) + 0.349(1.925)$$

$$\rho_s = \frac{14.5}{\left(1.925 \dfrac{Tz}{p} + 0.826 \right)}$$

where ρ_s, T, p, and z are as previously defined.

Study Committee
Biographical Information

Committee on the Analysis of Causes of the *Deepwater Horizon* Explosion, Fire, and Oil Spill to Identify Measures to Prevent Similar Accidents in the Future

Donald C. Winter, *Chair,* is Professor of Engineering Practice in the Department of Naval Architecture and Marine Engineering at the University of Michigan. He served as the 74th Secretary of the Navy from January 2006 to March 2009. As Secretary of the Navy, he led America's Navy and Marine Corps team and was responsible for an annual budget in excess of $125 billion and almost 900,000 people. Previously, Dr. Winter served as a corporate vice president and president of Northrop Grumman's Mission Systems sector. In that position he oversaw operation of the business and its 18,000 employees, providing information technology systems and services; systems engineering and analysis; systems development and integration; scientific, engineering, and technical services; and enterprise management services. Dr. Winter also served on the company's corporate policy council. Previously, he served as president and CEO of TRW Systems; vice president and deputy general manager for group development of TRW's Space and Electronics business; and vice president and general manager of the Defense Systems Division of TRW. From 1980 to 1982, he was with the Defense Advanced Research Projects Agency as program manager for space acquisition, tracking, and pointing programs. Dr. Winter received a doctorate in physics from the University of Michigan. He is also a graduate of the University of Southern California Management Policy Institute; the University of California, Los Angeles, Executive Program; and the Harvard University Program for Senior Executives in National and International Security. In 2002, he was elected a member of the National Academy of Engineering.

Paul M. Bommer is a senior lecturer in petroleum engineering in the Department of Petroleum and Geosystems Engineering at the University of Texas at

Austin. He is a major contributor to publications of the University of Texas Petroleum Extension Service, including books on oil well drilling and fundamentals of petroleum. Recently, Dr. Bommer was a member of the National Oceanic and Atmospheric Administration–U.S. Geological Survey Flow Rate Technical Group concerning oil rate estimates escaping from the BP Mississippi Canyon 252-001 (Macondo) well. In 1979, he cofounded Bommer Engineering Company, which is an oil and gas consulting company specializing in drilling and production operations and oil and gas appraisals. He is a registered professional engineer in the state of Texas. He received a PhD in petroleum engineering from the University of Texas at Austin.

Chryssostomos Chryssostomidis is the Doherty Professor of Ocean Science and Engineering at the Massachusetts Institute of Technology (MIT). In 1970, he was appointed to the faculty of MIT. In 1982 he was made a full professor and was appointed director of the MIT Sea Grant College Program. In 1989 he established the MIT Sea Grant Autonomous Underwater Vehicles Laboratory to develop technology and systems for advanced autonomous surface and underwater vehicles. His more than 100 publications display his wide range of interests. Among them are design methodology for ships; vortex-induced response of flexible cylinders; underwater vehicle design; and design issues in advanced shipbuilding, including the all-electric ship and T-craft. Professor Chryssostomidis is a licensed engineer in the state of Massachusetts and has served on several National Research Council (NRC) committees focusing on shipbuilding and marine issues. He received a PhD in ship systems analysis from MIT.

David E. Daniel is President of the University of Texas at Dallas. Previously, he was Dean of Engineering at the University of Illinois. Earlier, Dr. Daniel was L. B. Meaders Professor of Engineering at the University of Texas at Austin, where he taught for 15 years. He has conducted research in the area of geoenvironmental engineering, including research on drilling fluids, containment and management of those fluids, and fluid pressure control in the subsurface. Dr. Daniel served as chair of the American Society of Civil Engineers' External Review Panel, which evaluated the failure of the New Orleans levees. He also served as a member of NRC's Nuclear and Radiation Studies Board, the Board on Energy and Environmental Systems, and the Geotechnical Board. Dr. Daniel received a PhD in civil engineering from the University of Texas at Austin. He was elected to the National Academy of Engineering in 2000.

Thomas J. Eccles is a Rear Admiral in the U.S. Navy. He currently serves as Chief Engineer and Deputy Commander for Naval Systems Engineering, Naval Sea Systems Command (NAVSEA). Previously, he served at sea aboard the USS *Richard B. Russell* (SSN-687) and the USS *Gurnard* (SSN-662). He served as an engineering duty officer at Mare Island Naval Shipyard, as project officer for the USS *Parche* (SSN-683), and as assistant program manager for deep ocean engineering in the Navy's Deep Submergence Systems Program. He served twice in the Virginia Class Submarine Program, directing design and construction. He was executive assistant to the Commander, NAVSEA. Rear Admiral Eccles was Seawolf program manager through the delivery of the USS *Jimmy Carter* (SSN-23), where his team was awarded the Meritorious Unit Commendation, then program manager for Advanced Undersea Systems, responsible for research and development submarines, submarine escape and rescue systems, and atmospheric diving systems. He was also program manager for the design and construction of the unmanned autonomous submarine *Cutthroat* (LSV-2). His previous flag officer assignments included deputy commander for Undersea Warfare and Undersea Technology in NAVSEA and commander of the Naval Undersea Warfare Center. He received an MS from MIT in mechanical engineering, a naval engineer degree, and a master's degree in management from MIT's Sloan School.

Edmund P. Giambastiani, Jr., is a retired U.S. Navy Admiral. He served as the seventh Vice Chairman of the Joint Chiefs of Staff (the nation's second-highest-ranking military officer) from 2005 until he retired in 2007. While Vice Chairman, he also served as the cochair of the Defense Acquisition Board; chair of the Joint Requirements Oversight Council; and member of the National Security Council Deputies Committee, the Nuclear Weapons Council, and the Missile Defense Executive Board. He previously served as Commander, U.S. Joint Forces Command; as the North Atlantic Treaty Organization's first Supreme Allied Commander Transformation; and as senior military assistant to the U.S. Secretary of Defense. Admiral Giambastiani is a career nuclear submarine officer and gained extensive operational experience, including command at the submarine, squadron, and fleet levels and service as a chief engineer. His operational assignments included several in which he was responsible for demanding at-sea operations and for the development of new technologies and experimental processes. He commanded Submarine *NR-1*, the Navy's only nuclear-powered deep-diving ocean engineering and research submarine, the USS *Richard B. Russell* (SSN-687), and the Submarine Force U.S. Atlantic Fleet. He currently serves on the boards of the Boeing Company, Monster Worldwide, and the Mitre Corporation and consults independently. Since retirement, he has served on a number of U.S. government advisory boards, investigations, and task forces for the Secretaries of Defense and State and for the Director of the Central Intelligence Agency. He currently serves as chairman of the Secretary of the Navy's Advisory Panel. Admiral Giambastiani graduated from the U.S. Naval Academy with leadership distinction.

David A. Hofmann is Professor of Organizational Behavior at the University of North Carolina's Kenan-Flagler Business School. Dr. Hofmann conducts research on leadership, organizational and work group safety climates, and organizational factors that affect the safety behavior and performance of individual employees. His research has contributed significantly to the scientific foundation of tools used to assess the safety and organizational climates of organizations—

such as at the National Aeronautics and Space Administration after the *Columbia* accident—and to help plan interventions to improve safety climate. His research has appeared in *Academy of Management Journal, Academy of Management Review, Journal of Applied Psychology, Journal of Management, Organizational Behavior and Human Decision Processes*, and *Personnel Psychology*. He has published or has forthcoming numerous book chapters on leadership, safety issues, and multilevel research methods. In 2003, he edited a scholarly book on safety in organizations (*Health and Safety in Organizations: A Multilevel Perspective*), and he has a second edited book forthcoming on *Errors in Organizations*. He has received the American Psychological Association's Decade of Behavior Award and the Society of Human Resource Management's Yoder-Heneman Award, and he has been a Fulbright Senior Scholar. Before arriving at the University of North Carolina at Chapel Hill, he was a faculty member at Purdue University, Texas A&M University, and Michigan State University. Dr. Hofmann consults, conducts applied research, and leads executive workshops for a variety of governmental organizations and private corporations. He received a PhD in industrial and organizational psychology from Pennsylvania State University.

Roger L. McCarthy is a private engineering consultant and a director of Shui on Land, Ltd., which is involved in large-scale urban redevelopment in the People's Republic of China. Dr. McCarthy has substantial experience in the analysis of failures of an engineering or scientific nature. He has investigated the grounding of the *Exxon Valdez*, the explosion and loss of the *Piper Alpha* oil platform in the North Sea, the fire and explosion on the semisubmersible *Glomar Arctic II*, and the rudder failure on the very large crude carrier *Amoco Cadiz*. Previously, Dr. McCarthy was chairman emeritus of Exponent, Inc., and chairman of Exponent Science and Technology Consulting Company, Ltd. (Hangzhou, China). In 1992, he was appointed by the first President Bush to the President's Commission on the National Medal of Science. Dr. McCarthy received a PhD in mechanical engineering from MIT. He was elected to the National Academy of Engineering in 2004.

Najmedin Meshkati is Professor of Engineering at the University of Southern California. As a Jefferson Science Fellow, he served as a senior science and engineering adviser to the Office of the Science and Technology Adviser to the Secretary of State (2009–2010). For the past 25 years, he has been teaching and conducting research on risk reduction and reliability enhancement of complex technological systems, including those in the nuclear power, aviation, and petrochemical and transportation industries. He has written many articles on human factors, safety culture, and accident causation. Dr. Meshkati has inspected many petrochemical and nuclear power plants around the world, including Chernobyl in 1997. He worked with the U.S. Chemical Safety and Hazard Investigation Board as an expert adviser in human factors and safety culture on the investigation of the BP Refinery explosion in Texas City. He was elected Fellow of the

Human Factors and Ergonomics Society in 1997. Dr. Meshkati served as a member of the NRC Committee on Human Performance, Organizational Systems, and Maritime Safety. He also served as a member of the Marine Board's Subcommittee on Coordinated R&D Strategies for Human Performance to Improve Marine Operations and Safety. Dr. Meshkati received a PhD in industrial and systems engineering from the University of Southern California.

Keith K. Millheim is director and owner of Strategic Worldwide, LLC, which provides advisory services to oil companies for oil and gas exploration and production. He is also managing director of Nautilus International, LLC, which conducts research and development projects pertaining to deepwater well intervention and early deepwater reservoir appraisal. In 2007, he retired from Anadarko Petroleum Corporation as a distinguished adviser. He was also director of the Mewbourne School of Petroleum Engineering at the University of Oklahoma in Norman; director of the Institute of Drilling, Production, and Economics at the Mining University of Leoben in Austria; a research consultant and drilling manager for Amoco Production Company; and a petroleum engineer for Conoco. Dr. Millheim's research interests focus on the implementation of new technology in petroleum drilling. He has experience in deepwater drilling in the Gulf of Mexico, Brazil, the North Sea, and West Africa. He currently serves as a member of the NRC Committee on the Review of the Scientific Accomplishments and Assessment of the Potential for Future Transformative Discoveries with U.S.-Supported Scientific Ocean Drilling. Dr. Millheim received a PhD in mining engineering from the University of Leoben. He was elected to the National Academy of Engineering in 1990.

M. Elisabeth Paté-Cornell is Burt and Deedee McMurtry Professor and Past Chair of the Department of Management Science and Engineering at Stanford University. Her specialty is engineering risk analysis with application to complex systems (space, medical, etc.). Her research has focused on explicit consideration of human and organizational factors in the analysis of failure risks and, recently, on the use of game theory in risk analysis. Applications in the past few years have included counterterrorism and nuclear counterproliferation problems. She is a member of several boards, including those of Aerospace, Draper, and InQtel. She was a member of the President's Foreign Intelligence Advisory Board until December 2008. She received a PhD in engineering–economic systems from Stanford University. Dr. Paté-Cornell was elected to the National Academy of Engineering in 1995.

Robert F. Sawyer is the Class of 1935 Professor of Energy, Emeritus, with the Department of Mechanical Engineering at the University of California, Berkeley. His research interests are in combustion, pollutant formation and control, regulatory policy, rocket propulsion, and fire safety. He served as chairman of the California Air Resources Board, chairman of the energy and resources group of the University of California at Berkeley, chief of the liquid systems analysis section at the U.S. Air Force Rocket Propulsion Laboratory, and president of the Combustion Institute. Dr. Sawyer has served on numerous NRC committees and is a member of NRC's Board on Environmental Studies and Toxicology. He holds a PhD in aerospace science from Princeton University. He was elected to the National Academy of Engineering in 2008.

Jocelyn E. Scott is chief engineer and vice president of DuPont Engineering, Facilities and Real Estate. She joined DuPont in 1984 in the DuPont Photosystems and Electronic Products division in Rochester, New York. Ms. Scott served in numerous engineering and operations activities and carried out R&D assignments in various DuPont businesses. She was manager for various engineering positions and was named executive assistant to the chairman and CEO. In 2002, she was named director of DuPont Engineering and Research Technology, and in 2004 she became director of Capital Asset Productivity. In 2006 she was named director of DuPont Leveraged Operations; later that year, she became managing director, Facilities and Capital Asset Productivity. She was named vice president of DuPont Engineering in January 2008 and appointed to her current position in September 2008. Ms. Scott chaired the 2008 national conference of the Construction Users Roundtable. In addition to participating on various industry advisory boards, she has served on the Committee of Visitors for the Division of Chemical, Bioengineering, Environmental, and Transport Systems of the National Science Foundation. She received a master's degree in chemical engineering practice from MIT.

Arnold F. Stancell is Turner Professor of Chemical Engineering, Emeritus, at Georgia Institute of Technology. Earlier in his career he was offered tenure at MIT but decided on a career in industry. He had a 31-year career with Mobil Oil, where he was Vice President, U.S. Exploration and Production, offshore and onshore, and subsequently Vice President, International Exploration and Production for Europe, including the United Kingdom, Norway, the Netherlands and Germany, and the Middle East including Saudi Arabia, Qatar, and Abu Dhabi. He led the development of the now $70 billion natural gas production and liquefied natural gas joint venture between Mobil and Qatar. Previously, he held senior executive positions in Chemicals and Marketing and Refining. He started in Mobil in 1962 in research and development and has nine U.S. patents in petrochemical processes. Dr. Stancell received an ScD in chemical engineering from MIT; his thesis was on reservoir rock wettability and oil recovery. He is a licensed professional engineer in New York and Connecticut. He was elected to the National Academy of Engineering in 1997.

Mark D. Zoback is the Benjamin M. Page Professor of Geophysics at Stanford University. He is also codirector of the Stanford Rock Physics and Borehole Geophysics industrial consortium. Dr. Zoback conducts research on in situ stress, fault mechanics, and reservoir geomechanics. He is the author of a textbook, *Reservoir Geomechanics*, and was co–principal investigator of SAFOD, the scientific drilling project that drilled and sampled the San Andreas Fault at a depth of 3 km. He serves as a senior adviser to Baker Hughes, Inc. Before joining Stanford in 1984, Dr. Zoback worked at the U.S. Geological Survey, where he served as chief of the Tectonophysics Branch. He is the 2008 recipient of the Walter H. Bucher Medal from the American Geophysical Union. He received a PhD in geophysics from Stanford University. He was elected to the National Academy of Engineering in 2011.